SECONDARY SCHOOL EVALUATIVE CRITERIA:
NARRATIVE EDITION (REVISED)

A Guide For School Improvement

NATIONAL STUDY OF SCHOOL EVALUATION

Contents

Foreword

Since 1933 the National Study of School Evaluation (under this and two predecessor names) has been developing and providing instruments to effectively assess educational programs at the elementary, middle and secondary school levels. Recently an instrument to assess the central or district office in its entirety has been published. Each of these instruments has been carefully prepared, field tested nationwide and refined with the major goal of providing a means to evaluate, and thereby, improve the educational programs involved.

The *Secondary School Evaluative Criteria: Narrative Edition* (Revised) is the result of a major effort by the National Study of School Evaluation to revise and update the 1975 version. A special effort has been made to accommodate those aspects of independent and church-related schools that differ from public schools.

The work of the National Study of School Evaluation has been carried on by a Board of Directors composed of appointed representatives of the six regional accrediting associations. The Board has been involved in the development and revision of this instrument and has received the proposed materials and suggested additional refinements prior to final publication. Many of the present board members brought experiences with earlier publications of the National Study to bear on the preparation of this revised edition. It is the belief of the Board of Directors that the revised instrument is an effective evaluation instrument for schools.

The names of former members of the NSSE Board of Directors, listed according to the associations they represented, are as follows:

Middle States Association: Everett A. Adams, Rollin P. Baldwin, Marguerite S. Benthall, Paul R. Bingaman, Thomas J. Bradshaw, Mary H. Carter, Claude C. Casey, Jr., William H. Etsweiler, Jr., Harold A. Ferguson, E. D. Grizzell, Richard M. Gummere, William P. Hall, Earle T. Hawkins, Carl F. Hensinger, Archie R. Jordan, William Mather Lewis, George William McClelland, Karl G. Miller, Walter J. O'Conner, O. Meredith Parry, Edward B. Rooney, S.J., J. Folwell Scull, Jr., John A. Stoops, Arnold B. Swift, Charles C. Tillinghast, Anthony Wallace, F.S.C., William H. Warner, Thomas E. Warren, William A. Wetzel.

New England Association: James F. Baker, Richard J. Bradley, Richard H. Breen, Clarence I. Chatto, Howard Conant, Jesse B. Davis, John F. Donovan, William W. Dunn, Vincent Durnan, Donald W. Fowler, Raymond Green, Robert Long, Arthur W. Lowe, Carl Magnuson, Daniel Maloney, T. Holmes Moore, Herbert B. Moore, Francis Mullen, Robert J. O'Donnell, Maurice J. O'Leary, Francis P. Pellegrino, Ralph O. West.

North Central Association: Brother I. Basil, George C. Bell, Kenneth A. Berg, George E. Carrothers, Gordon Cawelti, Carl G. Franzen, A. J. Gibson, J. T. Giles, Merritt Jensen, J. Sandifer Keas, L. R. Kilzer, W. E. McVey, Wilfred M. Mallon, Donald C. Manlove, H. C. Mardi, Charles R. Maxwell, Harold H. Metcalf, Wilbert Mick, Floyd A. Miller, Jack Moore, E. E. Morley, M. R. Owens, Vernon D. Pace, A. A. Reed, W. S. Roe, Robert E. Stake, John A. Stanavage, Donald J. Stout, L. A. VanDyke, Elmer M. Weltzin, N.G. Wiltse.

Northwest Association: D. A. Emerson, George H. Fields, William L. Garner, Clifford A. Harmala, Henry M. Hart, Stowell R. Johnstone, William I. King, Clyde M. Martin, M. P. Moe, Cliff Robinson, Philip Soulen, Fred Stetson.

Southern Association: Harold P. Adams, M. L. Altstetter, T. P. Baker, E. C. Bolmeier, Raymond Christian, George D. Clark, Jr., Robert B. Clem, Joseph H. Cosby, Raymond Green, J. Henry Highsmith, Joseph M. Johnston, W. B. Killibrew, John H. Lounsbury, Idanelle McMurry, Joseph Roemer, A. J. St. Dizier, John J. Santillo, William R. Smithey, R. B. Sparks, T. Q. Srygley, Futrelle L. Temple, S. B.Tinsley, Robert Webb, C. R. Wilcox, Floyd Worley.

Western Association: A. J. Cloud, Thomas F. Damon, Donald R. McKinley, William M. Proctor, Joseph H. Pynchon, Robert L. Reeves.

Advisory Members: Arthur S. Adams, E. J. Ashbaugh, Paul Elicker, D. H. Gardner, J. Dan Hull, Galen Jones, Owen B. Kiernan, Ernest N. Mannino, William J. McGucken, William N. McGowan, M. E. Mushletz, William L. Pharis, John R. Proffitt, S. D. Shankland, J. W. Studebaker, Ellsworth Tompkins, Logan Wilson, George F. Zook.

Officers and staff of the Cooperative Study and the National Study since the beginning are listed below:

General Committee
Chairmen:

George E. Carrothers	1933–51
E. D. Grizzell	1951–56
Harold P. Adams	1956–57
Floyd A. Miller	1957–64
Mary H. Carter	1964–68
Richard J. Bradley	1968–78
H. Durell Ruffin	1978–80

Board of Directors

Chairman:	H. Durell Ruffin	1980–
Secretary:	Carl A. Jessen	1933–51
Executive Secretaries:	Carl A. Jessen	1951–60
	Roderic D. Matthews	1960–70
	Donald C. Manlove	1970–80
Executive Directors:	Donald C. Manlove	1980–83
	Vernon D. Pace	1983–
Business Manager:	Helen McGraw	1970–

The staff for research and development for the several publications of the Cooperative Study and the National Study consisted of the following:

Evaluative Criteria, 1940 edition: Walter C. Eells, M. L. Altstetter, Kenneth W. Eells
Evaluative Criteria, 1950 edition: Roy O. Billett, Roderic D. Matthews, James F. Baker
Evaluative Criteria, 1960 edition: Roderic D. Matthews, Carl A. Jessen, Lorenzo K. Reeds, S. J.
Evaluative Criteria for Junior High Schools: Roderic D. Matthews
Evaluative Criteria, 4th Edition: Charles Edwards
Junior High School/Middle School Evaluative Criteria: Donald C. Manlove, Lyle Mowrey
Elementary School Evaluative Criteria: Donald C. Manlove, John Davis
Evaluation Guidelines for Multicultural/Multiracial Education: John Stanavage
Student Opinion Inventory: Donald C. Manlove, Jan Perney
Secondary School Evaluative Criteria: Narrative Edition: Donald C. Manlove, Lawrence Keller
Teacher Opinion Inventory: Donald C. Manlove, Floyd A. Coppedge
Parent Opinion Inventory: Donald C. Manlove, Robert C. Stevens
Elementary School Evaluative Criteria, Audio-Filmstrip: Donald C. Manlove, Vernon D. Pace
Evaluative Criteria, 5th Edition: Robert L. Buser, Donald C. Manlove
Evaluative Criteria, 5th Edition, Audio-Filmstrip: Donald C. Manlove, Vernon D. Pace
Middle School/Junior High School Evaluative Criteria: Donald C. Manlove, Vernon D. Pace
Middle School/Junior High School Evaluative Criteria, Audio-Filmstrip: Donald C. Manlove, Sharon O'Bryan
Training Evaluators, Audio-Filmstrip: Donald C. Manlove, Vernon D. Pace
Elementary School Evaluative Criteria, Second Edition: Donald C. Manlove, Robert E. Ciscell
Central Office Evaluative Criteria: Donald C. Manlove, Robert E. Ciscell
K-12 School Evaluative Criteria: Donald C. Manlove, Vernon D. Pace, Susan K. Ramp
School Evaluation Simulation: Robert E. Ciscell, Vernon D. Pace
A Self-Directed Program for Developing Teacher and Administrator Evaluation Procedures: Robert L. Buser, Vernon D. Pace
Secondary School Evaluative Criteria: Narrative Edition (Revised): Donald C. Manlove, Vernon D. Pace

The members of the Board of Directors have long been aware of the importance of evaluation to the educational enterprise. The demands for effective instruments of evaluation at all school levels will be even greater in the future. The National Study, with your assistance, stands ready to meet the demands of the future.

BOARD OF DIRECTORS
National Study of School Evaluation

Acknowledgements

We wish to thank the many persons who contributed to the revision of the *Secondary School Evaluative Criteria: Narrative Edition* through service as field test participants and by way of suggestions made directly to the project director. Our sincere appreciation is extended to the following persons who gave of their time and expertise during the revision project.

Sister Mary Daniel Bohren
Teacher
Sisters of St. Joseph
Erie, Pennsylvania

Odette D. Harris
Principal
William Penn High School
Philadelphia, Pennsylvania

Michael J. Guerra
Executive Director
Secondary School Department
National Catholic Educational Association
Washington, D.C.

Nile F. Hunt
Consultant
North Carolina Secondary Committee
Raleigh, North Carolina

Mary Jean Johnson
Principal
Granger High School
West Valley City, Utah

Joseph M. Johnston
Executive Director
Commission on Secondary Schools
Southern Association of Colleges and Schools
Atlanta, Georgia

Edward W. Jones
Principal
Greenfield Senior High School
Greenfield, Massachusetts

James W. Keefe
Director of Research
National Association of Secondary School Principals
Reston, Virginia

Lawrence F. Keller
Director
Independent Study Division
Indiana University
Bloomington, Indiana

Robin Lester
Headmaster
Trinity Episcopal School Corporation
New York, New York

Fred J. Petersen
Associate Dean
School of Education
University of South Dakota
Vermillion, South Dakota

H. Durell Ruffin
Executive Director
Commission on Elementary Schools
Southern Association of Colleges and Schools
Atlanta, Georgia

Frank Starnes
Associate Superintendent for Secondary Schools
Garden Grove Unified School District
Garden Grove, California

Terry Tofte
State Director
North Central Association of Colleges and Schools
St. Paul, Minnesota

Donald C. Manlove
Project Director
Professor Emeritus
Indiana University
Bloomington, Indiana

Vernon D. Pace
Editor
Executive Director
National Study of School Evaluation
Indiana University
Bloomington, Indiana

Manual

Contents of the Manual

NATIONAL STUDY OF SCHOOL EVALUATION
5201 Leesburg Pike, Falls Church, Virginia 22041

The Purpose of the Manual

The purpose of the "Manual" is to describe the organization of the *Secondary School Evaluative Criteria: Narrative Edition* (Revised) and to provide directions for its use in the evaluation process. Guidelines for conducting the self-evaluation by individual schools and the evaluation by a visiting committee are presented with the understanding that when accreditation is involved, procedures may vary somewhat from state to state and region to region.

Organization of the Criteria

The *Secondary School Evaluative Criteria: Narrative Edition* (Revised) is composed of fourteen sections as follows:

M   Manual
N 1 School and Community (Public Schools)
N 2 School and Community (Nonpublic Schools)
O   Philosophy and Objectives
P   Design of Curriculum
Q   Instructional Areas
R   Individual Faculty Data
S   School Staff and Administration
T   Learning Media Services
U   Guidance Services
V   Auxiliary Services
W   Student Activities Program
X   School Plant and Facilities
Y   Plans and Priorities

The "Manual" provides an overview of the evaluation process and explains in some detail how the materials may be used. The section on "School and Community" together with the section on "Philosophy and Objectives" form the foundation for the process and undergird the entire evaluation.

"School and Community" is a data-gathering section. The section "School and Community (Nonpublic Schools)" is designed specifically for use by independent, church-related and other nonpublic schools. "Philosophy and Objectives" is designed to assist in developing or reexamining the school's existing philosophy and objectives in light of the data provided by the "School and Community" section.

The next two sections, "Design of Curriculum" and "Instructional Areas," are also closely related. "Design of Curriculum" focuses on the organization of the curriculum. It is extremely important that the subcommittee completing this section is a representative body of the total school program. The "Instructional Areas" section makes possible the evaluation of each of the areas of learning that the school identifies.

The section on "Individual Faculty Data" includes data concerning individual faculty members and provides an opportunity for those persons to express opinions on certain aspects of the school program. This is the only section that each faculty member completes individually. The "School Staff and Administration" section gives attention to administration, instructional staff and auxiliary staff. The "Learning Media Services" section includes media services, library and audio-visual services. The "Guidance Services" section includes information about personal, educational and career counseling and the guidance program. The section entitled "Auxiliary Services" provides for the examination of such services as those dealing with health, food and transportation.

The "Student Activities Program" section focuses on the school's total activities program. The next section deals with the school plant and facilities. The final section, "Plans and Priorities," provides an opportunity to place in priority the school's plans for improvement.

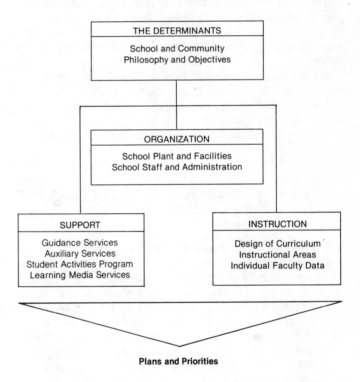

Plans and Priorities

The sections P, Q, S, T, U, V, W and X use this common format:

   I. Principles
  II. Description
 III. Evaluation
 IV. Plans for Improvement
  V. Current Status Scale

This five-part format begins with Part I, a series of principles designed to stimulate thought and reflection about the school program. Part II consists of probing questions designed to elicit a description of the program or area under consideration. Part III provides an opportunity to appraise and evaluate the program described in the second part and Part IV asks for the school's plans for improvement. Part V gives the school an opportunity to indicate its status in comparison to an "optimum" program.

The School's Task in Evaluation

The complete evaluation of a school as recommended by the National Study of School Evaluation is a three-step process. The first step is a self-evaluation carried out by the faculty of the individual school. This step usually requires a minimum of one year. The second step is an evaluation by a visiting committee, which usually requires a minimum of three days. The third step is the school's consideration and follow-up of the findings of the evaluation.

The National Study of School Evaluation has developed a means for recognizing that schools which are quite different may be equally educationally sound. This concept involves the basic principle that a school shall be evaluated in terms of what it is striving to accomplish (its philosophy and objectives) and according to the extent to which it is meeting the needs of the students who are enrolled or for whom it is responsible. The philosophy and objectives of the school must be acceptable to some agency (a community, an accrediting association, a state department of education) if the evaluation is to be recognized beyond the confines of the school.

School staff and administration, parents, students and members of the governing body should be actively involved in this self-evaluation. It is important that all who are involved understand that the purpose of this self-study is to improve the quality of the school's program through the means of self-evaluation and a comprehensive examination of what is happening to students in the school environment.

It is important to recognize that no one section of the self-study is meant to stand alone. Each section has been designed to correlate with other sections to form a comprehensive self-evaluation. It is important that participants not become single-minded when working on a particular section and overlook the fact that the total evaluation does not rest on that particular section. Staff interaction is essential in bringing about change.

This instrument is designed for a wide variety of secondary schools. Therefore, some items may not be applicable to a particular school situation. Schools are reminded of their prerogative to strike or change words, so long as they do not misdirect the intent of a statement, but render it more relevant. In the event that an entire statement appears to be irrelevant, a school may decide it does not apply and explain its view in the space provided.

Finally, it is vital that each evaluation participant receives feedback on reports of all sections of the self-study and that each participant has an opportunity to express either agreement or disagreement with each report. Provisions should be made for modification of a report when advisable.

More detailed information may be found in the "Manual," Section M.

Conducting the Self-Evaluation

Materials For Evaluation

The first step in the self-evaluation is to obtain materials for the use of the staff. A bound copy of the *Secondary School Evaluation Criteria: Narrative Edition* (Revised) should be examined before additional materials are ordered. This copy may be placed in the professional library for reference purposes. After the "Manual" and other parts of the *Secondary School Evaluative Criteria: Narrative Edition* (Revised) has been read carefully, the materials needed for the total process should be secured. The amount of materials ordered will depend on the size of the school, its financial resources, the extent of participation desired and any requirements of the accrediting association or state department of education. Quantities indicated below will, in most cases, meet minimum requirements:

1. Three bound copies of the *Secondary School Evaluative Criteria: Narrative Edition* (Revised) for reference.
2. Three copies each of Sections M, N 1 or N 2, O, P, S, T, U, V, W, X and Y.
3. Three copies of Section Q for each subject area in which instruction is provided.
4. Two copies of Section R for each member of the professional staff.

The above suggestions represent a minimum order only. Schools will find it advantageous to order enough copies—in addition to the three copies of each of the various sections mentioned in items 2 and 3 above—so that each member of each subcommittee having responsibility for a section will have a copy of that section.

It is also desirable to have sufficient copies of Sections N and O so that each member of the visiting committee may have a copy. Materials may be purchased from National Study of School Evaluation, 5201 Leesburg Pike, Falls Church, Virginia 22041.

If school personnel have had little experience with evaluations, it is highly advisable to invite a qualified person to work with them in the initial stages of the self-study. The values, procedures, problems and materials can be considered in such discussions.

Duties of the Steering Committee

The second step in the self-evaluation is selection of a steering committee to have responsibility for planning and supervising the entire self-evaluation of the school. The size of this committee may depend upon the size of the faculty, but generally a small committee is more effective; in most schools five to seven members are enough. The principal may be a member of the committee. This committee has primary responsibility for naming the members of all subcommittees, setting up a time schedule for the self-evaluation, establishing a method and a schedule for subcommittee reports, anticipating the need for and delivering materials and supplies to subcommittees and coordinating the work of all subcommittees and the reports of the faculty. In addition, the steering committee acts as a quality control on subcommittee reports. Since the self-evaluation is an extremely important part of the total evaluation, sufficient time should be allowed for it to be done well. The steering committee, in most instances, should be appointed at least one year before the evaluation is to be completed.

Work of Subcommittees

Normally each member of the staff will serve on at least two committees, one dealing with a general section and the other dealing with a learning area. When appropriate, district-wide personnel should participate in the self-evaluation process.

Section N, "School and Community," provides data that are basic to the entire evaluation. The subcommittee responsible for this area should begin immediately to collect the data for its report. This report should be presented to the faculty before work is begun on the other sections. Section O, "Philosophy and Objectives," is the other basic section upon which an evaluation rests. The subcommittee responsible for this area should develop its philosophy and objectives or reexamine its existent philosophy and objectives in light of the data provided by the "School and Community" report and determine its relevancy to the present school program. This section also should be presented to the faculty for discussion and approval before work on other sections is begun.

All members of the teaching staff should then reexamine their specialized instructional areas to determine whether the objectives and teaching practices are consistent with the stated philosophy and objectives of the school.

The other subcommittees should then be appointed. It is important that specialists and generalists serve on each sub-committee. For example, the subcommittee on mathematics should include teachers of mathematics and some teachers from other areas. The subcommittee on staff and administration should include members of the administration as well as some staff members not involved directly in administration. The self-evaluation will be more valid and the total program of the school will be better understood by all members of the staff as a result of the efforts of these subcommittees. An effort should be made to include representatives from the various grade levels on all subcommittees. It should be noted that the subcommitees for Section P, "Design of Curriculum," and Section Y, "Plans and Priorities," need to have members who are representative of the entire school program since both are global sections.

Parents and students should play a role in the self-evaluation process. They can be represented on all subcommittees or on selected subcommittees. In addition, the opinions of both parents and students may be secured on a broad and organized basis through the use of NSSE's *Parent Opinion Inventory* and *Student Opinion Inventory*. These carefully constructed and validated instruments, administered to a sample of both of these key populations, make it possible to incorporate the views of these groups in the self-study process as a separate, but related, component.

The process of evaluation is of utmost importance in the self-study. This is the time when the subcommittees determine whether the philosophy and objectives are relevant and if they are being achieved. This information can be gathered via teacher-made tests, criterion-referenced tests, observations, checklists, etc. The subcommittees discover strengths and weaknesses in each area and, while retaining the strengths of the program, plan ways to improve the weaker aspects. The sections that follow the five-part format (Sections P, Q, S, T, U, V and W) are designed in a logical fashion.

Each evaluative section is introduced by a statement of principles. The principles encourage discussion within the subcommittees. Each subcommittee should examine the principles carefully and critically, modify them if desirable and indicate the degree of acceptance and implementation on the scales provided. These are followed by a description of the program, an evaluation of the program, recommendations for improvement and a determination as to the program's current status. Questions should be answered clearly and concisely. The subcommittee presents its completed report to the entire faculty for approval or modification.

The Visiting Committee

The complete evaluation of a school as recommended by the National Study of School Evaluation requires the services of a visiting committee. The purpose of the visiting committee is to provide a reaction to the self-evaluation carried out by the school staff. This objective review by professional colleagues not directly involved in the school program is necessary if the evaluation is to be used in an accreditation or approval process, and is valuable when the evaluation is used to interpret the work of the school to the community.

Representatives of each school, county, state, regional association or cooperating group of schools should study its own situation and determine size of committees, length of visits, schedules of visits, methods of selecting committee members and methods of financing the work of visiting committees.

Selection of Visiting Committee

The agency sponsoring the evaluation should select the members of the visiting committee. Typically, the sponsoring
agency (regional accrediting association, state committee, university or state department of education) should submit a proposed list of committee members to the head of the school to be evaluated for approval or rejection. It is usually advantageous to have both generalists and specialists on the committee. Invitations to serve on the committee should be sent by the sponsoring agency well in advance of the date of the visit. A return acceptance card with the name of the school to be visited and the dates of the visit should be sent with the invitation.

The selection of the chairman of the visiting committee should be agreed on several months before the visit.

The final list of visiting committee members should be sent to the head of the school and the chairman of the visiting committee at least one month before the date of the visit.

Size of Committee

The size of the visiting committee varies with the scope of the program to be evaluated, the enrollment of the school and the length of the visit. Committees of eleven to fifteen members staying from three to four days are not uncommon. If specialists in each area are used, the numbers on the committee will, of necessity, need to be increased. It is evident that schools with very large enrollments may need to use larger committees.

Professional Attitude of Members

The visit of a committee is a highly professional undertaking. The attitude of the members should be one of professional cooperation, helpfulness and constructive criticism. Members should observe, visit and inquire for the purpose of getting as comprehensive a view of the work of the school as is possible in the time available. Free discussion of the work of the school should be encouraged. Staff members of the school should be given an opportunity to fully explain what they are doing rather than be made to feel defensive. Individual members of the committee should avoid making criticisms or suggestions to members of the school staff even if asked to do so. All such suggestions should be discussed by the committee and, if accepted, be reflected in the final report. Nearly all of the adverse criticisms of the evaluation of schools grow out of the actions of individuals who disregard this principle.

Work of Visiting Committee

Detailed directions for visits have been prepared by many sponsoring agencies. The points that follow are given with the expectation that they may be modified or supplemented by these agencies:

1. The chairman of the visiting committee should visit the school prior to the date of the committee's visit. Sufficient time should be spent by the chairman to get acquainted with some of the staff, study the physical plant, the school schedule, the physical facilities and arrangements for the committee and discuss the visit with the administrative head of the school and the chairman of the steering committee. The chairman of the visiting committee should be responsible for determining that the self-evaluation has been completed and that the school is ready for the visiting committee. Arrangements for the committee should be discussed in detail with the principal and the chairman of the steering committee. The chairman of the visiting committee in consultation with the principal should work out a schedule of visiting committee activities.

2. The chairman should request information from members of the visiting committee about their areas of specialization and interest.

3. The head of the school to be visited should send the complete list of the visiting committee to each member of the visiting committee so that plans for sharing transportation can be made. This should be done as soon after receiving the list as possible. At the same time each visitor should be asked about what traveling and/or lodging accommodations will be required.

4. As soon as convenient, but at least two weeks before the date of the visit, the head of the school to be visited should send materials about the school to each member of the visiting committee. These materials should include directions for reaching the school, parking arrangements, copies of the self-evaluation reports on "School and Community," "Philosophy and Objectives" and any other sections of the self-evaluation report that are appropriate and printed booklets or materials about the school that will be useful in giving the visitor a more comprehensive picture. At the organization meeting, details of school administration, such as plans of buildings and grounds, activities scheduled for the visiting days, courses of studies, teachers' schedules (including room, subject taught, time and section), and similar materials should be distributed to the visitors.

5. The school, in making preparations for accommodating the visiting committee, should be aware of the time-consuming nature of the task and the desire of the visitors to do a superior job.

6. The agency sponsoring evaluations should prepare suggestions and information for visiting committees on expense accounts, general time schedule for a visit and any other matters that differ from suggestions included in this "Manual." Such a statement should be supplied to each visitor and may well be sent with the invitation to serve on a committee.

The Visit

The school should operate on a normal schedule during the visit of the committee. The visitors come to get as complete a picture of the school as possible in the limited time available. Since many seasonal phases of the year's program may not be seen, photographs, programs, press comments, and similar material concerning these phases should be collected, preserved and arranged for viewing by the committee.

Visits should start with an informal dinner or reception the first evening. Such a gathering gives the committee an opportunity to meet members of the faculty and the board of control. The chairman of the visiting committee may explain the procedures to be followed and thus set the tone for the visit. The principal or another staff member may summarize the reports on "School and Community" and "Philosophy and Objectives." The visiting committee must be fully aware of the nature of the student body and the community served by the school and have a clear understanding of the school's philosophy and objectives. Either before or after this meeting, the chairman will wish to meet with the other members of the visiting committee to complete the organization of the committee.

Organization of Committee

The chairman will have organized the subcommittees and notified each member of the assignment well in advance of the visit. At the organizational meeting the chairman will discuss the professional nature of the work of the visiting committee. He or she also should explain the importance of visitors observing what is done rather than telling what they (the visitors) do, the confidential nature of the committee's discussions, and the dangers of gossiping after the visit is completed.

Visiting Classes

Members of a subcommittee responsible for a given learning area should plan their classroom visits so that all teachers are observed. Care should also be taken to observe all the different varieties of work-content, level of difficulty, special objectives, sequence and so on. Visitors should enter classes unannounced, avoid participation in class activities, defer making notes until after leaving classrooms and leave with a minimum of disturbance.

The visit should be as informal as possible. Committee members may wish to talk to individual students but should not disturb formal learning groups to do so. No effort should be made to interview the teachers at this time; meetings with teachers should be scheduled for preparation periods or before or after school. If the work of a class is obviously to continue in much the same form for the entire period a visitor may leave after a short visit and return to observe at another time.

Observation provides a basis for making recommendations concerning teaching techniques, use of instructional media, and the quality of instruction. Each visitor should remember that there will be a chance to contribute to discussions of all aspects of the school. It is therefore important to notice physical facilities in classrooms and in other areas, attitudes of students toward their work, care of property, morale of students, cleanliness of building, safety precautions, use of display materials, work habits, condition and relevance of textbooks and other study materials and similar elements of the school program.

Investigating General Areas

Each member of the visiting committee is responsible for reviewing the self-evaluations and making recommendations in a general area such as "School Plant" or "Student Activities Program" and/or in a learning area. The report made by the school must be examined carefully and additional information obtained from either those who made the self-evaluation or other staff members. Formal conferences are scheduled to provide an opportunity to ask questions, but in most cases there will be special items that must be investigated. The additional investigations must be planned to be made between classes, before and after school and by appointment. Care must be exercised so that important conclusions or recommendations are based on sound information.

Members of each subcommittee should examine all the sections of the self-evaluation made by the school for which they are responsible, noting any changes that have been made in the text.

The Reports

The work of the visiting committee includes the construction of several types of reports. The members of subcommittees write reports on their respective areas, which contribute to the chairman's final written report to the school and to the sponsoring agency. Additionally, an oral report may be made by the chairman of the visiting committee to the staff or administration of the school being evaluated.

Subcommittee Reports

After studying the various areas, each subcommittee prepares a report consisting of at least four parts:
  a) A brief introductory description of the area;
  b) Strengths of the present program;
  c) Weaknesses, concerns and questions relating to the present program; and
  d) Recommendations for future consideration by the school personnel.
The visiting committee's schedule should provide time for the chairman of each subcommittee to report the substance of the above points to the entire committee. Sufficient discussion should follow each report in order to reach consensus and thereby to have the commendations, concerns and recommendations supported by the entire visiting committee. In the event that consensus cannot be reached after a period of discussion, the chairman is responsible for accommodating the several positions in an appropriate manner in the final report.

After reports have been heard and accepted by the entire committee, they should be submitted to the chairman of the visiting committee for editing and integration into the committee's final report.

Oral Report

The oral report serves primarily as a means of concluding this part of the evaluation. It is a brief summary given by the committee chairman at the conclusion of the visit. It should include the general highlights of the visit and only broad, general conclusions. It contains a few commendations and a few general recommendations. It should be emphasized that the written report will be much more detailed and specific.

The oral report may be given to the entire faculty or to the administrative staff and members of the steering committee who transmit it to the faculty. Practice varies in different sections of the country.

Written Report

A final written report is recommended by the National Study of School Evaluation. The report is prepared by the chairman of the visiting committee and contains an introduction, the approved commendations and recommendations from the subcommitee reports and a concluding statement Each subcommittee report should include the introductory description that precedes its commendations, concerns and recommendations.

The chairman must accept the responsibility for the quality of the written report. The report should be carefully edited so that it is accurate, mechanically correct and free of ambiguous or incomplete statements. Much of the value of the entire evaluation process may be lost if the written report shows evidence of carelessness or hasty and thoughtless expression. Members of boards of control and the general public which oftentimes are not familiar with the procedures used in evaluations may read the report; therefore, it should be clear, self-explanatory and as free as possible of educational jargon. The agency sponsoring the evaluation should tell the chairman how many copies of the report are required and the policy on distribution.

Suggested Activities Following the Evaluation

Evaluation should be a stimulating force leading to definite improvements in the services offered by the school to its students and community. The entire process should include self-analysis of the school's programs and services, objective reaction to the school's analysis by a visiting committee, oral and written reports to the school by the chairman of the visiting committee and a resultant program of continuous improvement by the school.

Regional accrediting associations, state departments of education and local school systems have developed helpful guidelines for follow-up programs. In the absence of such guidelines by sponsoring agencies, the following suggestions, based on the experience of various schools, may be of value:

1. The principal and the staff should become familiar with the information contained in the written report of the visiting committee. The written report should be available to all school personnel so that they can be both familiar with its contents and ready to participate in the follow-up activities.
2. A "rest period" for the committees following the intensive visiting committee experience is usually desirable.

Schools normally retain the same committee structure for the planning and implementation of follow-up activities.

3. The follow-up activities may be expedited by placing all recommendations presented in the written report in one of the following categories:
   a) Recommendations that can be carried out immediately;
   b) Recommendations that can be carried out in the near future;
   c) Recommendations that may be carried out through long-term planning; and
   d) Recommendations that are judged to be invalid.
4. The written report may be presented to members of the school board and to the local parent-teacher association. The extent to which the public will be made familiar with the complete report is the responsibility of the school district. In schools where students and parents have assisted in the evaluative process, they will, of course, be interested in and concerned with the results.

Development of the Secondary School Evaluative Criteria: Narrative Edition

The establishment of standards for schools has been a gradual process. It began around the turn of the century when secondary schools and colleges belonging to the regional accrediting associations attempted to reach an agreement on the entrance requirements for the various colleges. The youthful regional associations also began the task of developing accreditation procedures for those schools that desired to meet the standards for membership in the associations.

With the formation of the Cooperative Study of Secondary School Standards in 1933, the emphasis in school evaluation changed from the maintenance of minimum standards to achievement of excellence in all aspects of a school's work. The Cooperative Study of Secondary School Standards was administered by a General Committee composed of representatives of the six regional accrediting associations. In June 1959, the name was changed to the National Study of Secondary School Evaluation. Because of needs of regional associations and schools to give attention to the evaluation of junior high schools and elementary schools, the name was changed again in November 1969, to the National Study of School Evaluation.

The work of the National Study of School Evaluation through the years has produced the 1940, 1950, 1960, 4th Edition and 5th Edition of the *Evaluative Criteria for Secondary Schools.* Thousands of educators have been involved in the development of the *Evaluative Criteria,* and their combined efforts have continued to influence the change from maintaining minimum standards to striving for excellence in all aspects of a school's work.

In February 1962, the General Committee of the National Study directed that a plan be developed for the publication of materials for the evaluation of junior high schools. Eighteen junior high school educators developed the *Evaluative Criteria for Junior High Schools,* which was an adaptation of the *Evaluative Criteria for Secondary Schools: 1960 Edition.*

The General Committee in 1965 decided to replace the *Evaluative Criteria for Junior High Schools* by the development of an instrument specifically designed to evaluate junior high schools and middle schools. That effort, involving hundreds of junior high school and middle school educators from across the nation, resulted in the publication of the new *Junior High School/Middle School Evaluative Criteria* in May 1970.

Because many educators have believed for some time that emphasis on evaluating and accrediting secondary schools is merely a partial solution to improved education, the Study conducted a national survey of key educators in 1969 to assess the desirability of developing an instrument to evaluate elementary schools. The results of the survey were overwhelmingly positive. A project to develop such an instrument was launched in 1970. Hundreds of elementary school educators participated in the project and a new *Elementary School Evaluative Criteria* was published in June 1973.

The *Junior High School/Middle School Evaluative Criteria* and the *Elementary School Evaluative Criteria* were designed and structured with an open-ended questionnaire format rather than the checklist format that has characterized the five editions of the *Evaluative Criteria*. This new approach was widely acclaimed by those who used it, and several secondary schools also reported following the format of the *Junior High School/Middle School Evaluative Criteria* with considerable success.

The great diversity among secondary schools of this nation suggest the desirability of providing more than one approach to evaluation. That fact coupled with the early reports of success in using the open-ended approach in some publications of the National Study prompted a decision to develop an alternate instrument for secondary schools. The decision was made in November 1972 by the Administrative Committee who agreed to serve as an ad hoc committee setting the direction for the new publication. This committee also decided that the new instrument would follow the structure and format of the *Elementary School Evaluative Criteria* and the *Junior High School/Middle School Evaluative Criteria*. The publication of the three instruments could then provide school systems with instrumentation for system wide evaluation.

The Executive Secretaries of the Commissions on Secondary Schools of the Regional Associations were asked to suggest names of knowledgeable individuals who might be willing to serve as members of a writing team to prepare the materials. From the suggested names a writing team was formed.

The team met on the Indiana University Bloomington campus March 11–14, 1973 to get an overview of the project and then to write, reflect, discuss and refine the materials. After this work session the materials were assembled and mailed to each member of the writing team for further review and comment.

The Executive Secretaries of the Commissions on Secondary Schools were then asked to suggest names of schools ready for an evaluation during the 1973-74 school year that might field test the new materials. This effort resulted in the selection of sixteen schools which were invited to participate in the field test. In selecting these pilot schools, consideration was given to enrollment, location, type of school and type of program in order to get as diversified a sample as possible. Each pilot school was provided by mail with an orientation to the project and copies of the new materials to be tested.

In addition to the data from the pilot schools, data were sought from the original writing team members who were asked to again review the materials.

The results of the field test and suggestions of the writing team members were analyzed and reviewed by the project staff and the materials refined accordingly. The proposed instrument was then mailed to all members of the General Committee for review. At the General Committee meeting in Mt. Pocono, Pennsylvania, in August 1974, recommenda-

tions for further refinement were discussed and made. These changes were made by the project staff and presented to the Administrative Committee in October 1974. At this time, the instrument was accepted for publication.

The *Secondary School Evaluative Criteria: Narrative Edition* came into wide use. In the years following the development of this instrument, some National Study of School Evaluation materials were revised. In 1978, the *Evaluative Criteria, 5th Edition* was published. To accompany this updated instrument was an audio-filmstrip. In 1979, the *Middle School/Junior High School Evaluative Criteria*, which also had an accompanying audio-filmstrip, was published. The *Elementary School Evaluative Criteria, Second Edition* and an audio-filmstrip were published in 1981.

The National Study of School Evaluation was also involved in developmental projects. Out of such projects came new items such as *Training Evaluators Audio-Filmstrip*, the *Central Office Evaluative Criteria*, *Student Opinion Inventory*, *Teacher Opinion Inventory*, *Parent Opinion Inventory*, *K-12 School Evaluative Criteria*, *School Evaluation Simulation* and *A Self-Directed Program for Developing Teacher and Administrator Evaluation Procedures*.

After several years, suggestions for improving the *Secondary School Evaluative Criteria: Narrative Edition* were made. Therefore, the National Study of School Evaluation began to receive requests that the instrument be revised; in the summer of 1981, the Board of Directors charged the Executive Director with this duty.

To help with the revision process, the regional accrediting associations were requested to provide the names of schools that would be using the *Secondary School Evaluative Criteria: Narrative Edition* in the 1982–83 school year. From this list, schools were selected that represented a wide geographic area and were diverse in nature. The schools were asked to participate in two ways: 1) subcommittees were to critique the *Secondary School Evaluative Criteria: Narrative Edition* as they used it in their self-study, and 2) all teachers were to respond to a questionnaire designed to locate items needing to be modified.

The schools participating in the field test were:

Carrollton High School, Carrollton, Ohio
Granger High School, Granger, Utah
Hanover High School, Hanover, New Hampshire
North Myrtle Beach High School, North Myrtle Beach,
    South Carolina
Oldfields School, Sparks, Maryland
The Ranney School, Tinton Falls, New Jersey

A Revision Committee representing the regional associations, the National Association of Secondary School Principals and the National Catholic Educational Association was appointed.

They were assigned two tasks: first, to critique the current instrument individually and submit their recommendations for changes and modifications, and second, to make collective judgments as committee members about the final revision of the instrument.

The data from the field test schools and the consultants were collected and compiled in a systematic fashion so as to be readily accessible to members of the Revision Committee. This group met in St. Petersburg Beach, Florida, April 27–30, 1983.

Each section of the *Secondary School Evaluative Criteria: Narrative Edition* was carefully reviewed, updated and revised in accordance with the information gathered by the project staff. In addition to the modification of current sections, some new parts and sections were added. A "Glossary" containing definitions of troublesome terms appears at the end of the "Manual," Section M. A new section, "School and Community" (Nonpublic Schools), Section N2 has been added. The former section on "Student Services" has been divided into "Guidance Services," Section U and "Auxiliary Services," Section V. Then a new section "Plans and Priorities," Section Y has been added. All former sections have been updated and revised.

After further refinements were made by the Executive Director, the newly revised instrument was presented to the National Study of School Evaluation Board of Directors in July 1983 and approved for publication. The *Secondary School Evaluative Criteria: Narrative Edition* (Revised) was published in 1984.

The National Study of School Evaluation wishes to thank all of the persons involved in this important revision project.

Supplemental Materials

Current Publications of the National Study of School Evaluation:

Evaluation Guidelines for Multicultural/Multiracial Education, 1973

Secondary School Evaluative Criteria: Narrative Edition, 1975

Evaluative Criteria, 5th Edition, 1978

Evaluative Criteria, 5th Edition Audio-Filmstrip, 1978

Middle School/Junior High School Evaluative Criteria, 1979

Middle School/Junior High School Evaluative Criteria Audio-Filmstrip, 1979

Training Evaluators Audio-Filmstrip, 1979

Elementary School Evaluative Criteria, Second Edition, 1981

Elementary School Evaluative Criteria, Second Edition Audio-Filmstrip, 1981

Central Office Evaluative Criteria, 1981

Student Opinion Inventory, Revised Edition, 1981

Teacher Opinion Inventory, Revised Edition, 1981

Parent Opinion Inventory, Revised Edition, 1981

K-12 School Evaluative Criteria, 1983

School Evaluation Simulation, 1984

A Self-Directed Program for Developing Teacher and Administrator Evaluation Procedures, 1984

Secondary School Evaluative Criteria: Narrative Edition (Revised), 1984

Use of Publications by Regional Accrediting Associations

Specific information relative to the use of these materials in the regional evaluation and accreditation process may be obtained from the six regional accrediting associations:

Middle States Association of Colleges and Schools, 3624 Market Street, Philadelphia, PA 19104

New England Association of Schools and Colleges, Inc., The Sanborn House, 15 High Street, Winchester, MA 01890

North Central Association of Colleges and Schools, Commission on Schools, 1540 30th Street, P.O. Box 18, Boulder, CO 80306

Northwest Association of Schools and Colleges, Commission on Schools, Blue Mountain Community College, Box 100, Pendleton, OR 97801

Southern Association of Colleges and Schools, 795 Peachtree Street, N.E., Atlanta, GA 30365

Western Association of Schools and Colleges, 1611 Rollins Road, Burlingame, CA 94010

Glossary

Administrative staff - refers to any or all of the following: superintendent, assistant superintendent(s), principal, assistant principal(s) and similar school personnel.

Articulation

horizontal - relationship of continuity existing among the various parts of a curriculum at a given level with respect to successive age and grade levels of instruction, such that, taken together, the parts have some degree of unity and coherence.

interdisciplinary - the process of bringing together teachers from many different fields of learning to plan a program that is relevant to all their approaches.

program - (1) the process of so arranging the instructional programs of the successive grades and divisions of the school system that a closely interlocking, continuous, and consistent educational environment is provided for pupils as they progress through the system; (2) the degree of continuity, consistency, and interdependence in the offerings of the successive grades and divisions of the school system.

vertical - the degree to which the interlocking and interrelation of the successive levels of the educational system facilitate the continuous, economical and efficient educational progress of pupils.

Auxiliary staff - includes clerical, custodial, paraprofessional, food services, transportation and similar nonprofessional staff.

Climate - the learning environment found in a school; this includes not only physical environment but emotional tone. The environment must provide a pleasant atmosphere and encourage productivity.

Curriculum - (1) a systematic group of courses or sequence of subjects required for graduation or certification in a major field of study, for example, social studies curriculum, physical education curriculum; (2) a general overall plan of the content or specific materials of instruction that the school should offer the student by way of qualifying him for graduation or certification or for entrance into a professional or vocational field; (3) a group of courses and planned experiences provided to a student under the guidance of the school or college (may refer to what is intended as planned courses and other activities or intended opportunities or experiences, or to what was actualized for the learner, as in actual educational treatment or all experiences of the learner under the direction of the school).

Ethnic group - a fairly distinct cultural group, whether racial, national, or tribal.

Exceptional student - a child who deviates intellectually, physically, socially or emotionally in his growth and development so markedly from what is considered to be normal that he cannot receive maximum benefit from a regular school program and requires a special class or supplementary instruction and services.

Governing body - an officially constituted group of persons charged with the overall responsibility for the control and management of the affairs of one or more educational institutions; usually delegates executive functions to appointed administrators and deals primarily with matters of policy.

Instructional staff - includes teachers, counselors and other professional persons not serving as administrators.

Integrated studies - a plan of instruction in which the traditional boundaries between subject fields are largely ignored and the basis of which is the development of study units and broad learning experiences in which cogent material from a number of fields is brought to bear on the main problem of each study unit or learning experience.

Learning areas - those subject areas that make up the curricular program.

Objective - aim, end in view, or purpose of a course of action or a belief; that which is anticipated as desirable in the early phases of an activity and serves to select, regulate, and direct later aspects of the act so that the total process is designed and integrated.

Philosophy - an integrated personal view that serves to guide the individual's conduct and thinking.

Professional growth - refers to all activities leading toward staff improvement and upgrading. This may include, but is not limited to, inservice training at the department, school or district level; workshops, conferences or course work for the instructional or administrative staffs.

Program development - a process by which the nature and sequence of future educational programs are determined.

Self-concept - the perception or notion that each person has of himself; the positive, neutral or negative view of one's own individual identity.

Semi skilled - those jobs requiring a limited amount of on-the-job training.

Skilled - those jobs requiring specific previous training.

Student activities, extraclass - that area of the total curriculum which includes experiences not usually provided in typical classes, such as camp experiences, clubs, assembly programs, interscholastic and intramural athletics, student participation in government and other activities under the guidance of the school; (The present trend is toward use of this term instead of "extracurricular activities," which is misleading in the light of the new definitions of the curriculum.)

Unskilled - those jobs that require no previous training.

Many of these definitions are from Good, Carter V. (ed). *Dictionary of Education.* New York: McGraw-Hill Book Company, 1973.

School and Community
(Public Schools)

NAME OF SCHOOL_____

DATE_____

Prepared by

_____   _____

_____   _____

_____   _____

The committee given the responsibility for completing this section will find it beneficial to become thoroughly familiar with the entire section before attempting to react or respond to any part of it.

This section, "School and Community," provides basic data for the complete evaluation. The importance of careful and accurate gathering of the data cannot be overemphasized. This section should be completed before work is started on the other sections.

Although space has been provided throughout the section for committee responses, statements need not be limited to that space; the committee should feel free to attach addenda for items whose clarity will be improved by fuller development.

The report of this committee, when completed, should be presented to the entire faculty for approval or modification.

NATIONAL STUDY OF SCHOOL EVALUATION
5201 Leesburg Pike, Falls Church, Virginia 22041

Organization of the Criteria

The *Secondary School Evaluative Criteria: Narrative Edition* (Revised) is composed of fourteen sections as follows:

M	Manual
N1	School and Community (Public Schools)
N2	School and Community (Nonpublic Schools)
O	Phliosophy and Objectives
P	Design of Curriculum
Q	Instructional Areas
R	Individual Faculty Data
S	School Staff and Administration
T	Learning Media Services
U	Guidance Services
V	Auxiliary Services
W	Student Activities Program
X	School Plant and Facilities
Y	Plans and Priorities

The "Manual" provides an overview of the evaluation process and explains in some detail how the materials may be used. The section on "School and Community" together with the section on "Philosophy and Objectives" form the foundation for the process and undergird the entire evaluation.

"School and Community" is a data-gathering section. The section "School and Community (Nonpublic Schools)" is designed specifically for use by independent, church-related and other nonpublic schools. "Philosophy and Objectives" is designed to assist in developing or reexamining the school's existing philosophy and objectives in light of the data provided by the "School and Community" section.

The next two sections, "Design of Curriculum" and "Instructional Areas," are also closely related. "Design of Curriculum" focuses on the organization of the curriculum. It is extremely important that the subcommittee completing this section is a representative body of the total school program. The "Instructional Areas" section makes possible the evaluation of each of the areas of learning that the school identifies.

The section on "Individual Faculty Data" includes data concerning individual faculty members and provides opportunity for those persons to express opinions on certain aspects of the school program. This is the only section that each faculty member completes individually. The "School Staff and Administration" section gives attention to administration, instructional staff and auxiliary staff. The "Learning Media Services" section includes media services, library and audio-visual services. The "Guidance Services" section includes information about personal, educational and career counseling and the guidance program. The section entitled "Auxiliary Services" examines such services as those dealing with health, food and transportation. The "Student Activities Program" section focuses on the school's total activities program. The next section deals with the school plant and facilities. The final section, "Plans and Priorities," provides an opportunity to place in priority the school's plans for improvement.

The sections P, Q, S, T, U, V, W, and X use this common format:

- I. Principles
- II. Description
- III. Evaluation
- IV. Plans for Improvement
- V. Current Status Scale

This five-point format begins with Part I, a series of principles designed to stimulate thought and reflection about the school program. Part II consists of probing questions designed to elicit a description of the program or area under consideration. Part III provides an opportunity to appraise and evaluate the program described in the second part and Part IV asks for the school's plans for improvement. Part V gives the school an opportunity to indicate its status in comparison to an "optimum" program.

The School's Task in Evaluation

The complete evaluation of a school as recommended by the National Study of School Evaluation is a three-step process. The first step is a self-evaluation carried out by the faculty of the individual school. This step usually requires a minimum of one year. The second step is an evaluation by a visiting committee, which usually requires a minimum of three days. The third step is the school's consideration and follow-up of the findings of the evaluation.

The National Study of School Evaluation has developed a means for recognizing that schools which are quite different may be equally sound educationally. This concept involves the basic principle that a school shall be evaluated in terms of what it is striving to accomplish (its philosophy and objectives) and according to the extent to which it is meeting the needs of the students who are enrolled or for whom it is responsible. The philosophy and objectives of the school must be acceptable to some agency (a community, an accrediting association, a state department of education) if the evaluation is to be recognized beyond the confines of the school.

School staff and administration, parents, students and members of the governing body should be actively involved in this self-evaluation. It is important that all who are involved understand that the purpose of this self-study is to improve the quality of the school's program through the means of self-evaluation and comprehensive examination of what is happening to students in the school environment.

It is important to recognize that no one section of the self-study is meant to stand alone. Each section has been designed to correlate with other sections to form a comprehensive self-evaluation. It is important that participants not become single-minded when working on a particular section and overlook the fact that the total evaluation does not rest on that particular section. Staff interaction is essential in bringing about change.

This instrument is designed for a wide variety of secondary schools. Therefore, some items may not be applicable to a particular school situation. Schools are reminded of their prerogative to strike or change words, so long as they do not misdirect the intent of a statement but render it more relevant. In the event that an entire statement appears to be irrelevant, a school may decide it does not apply and explain its view in the space provided.

Finally, it is vital that each evaluation participant receives feedback on reports of all sections of the self-study and that each participant have an opportunity to express either agreement or disagreement with each report. Provision should be made for modification of a report when advisable.

More detailed information may be found in the "Manual," Section M.

Statement of Purpose

The evaluation of a school must, to a large extent, be based on the degree to which its educational programs meet the needs of students in the community it serves.

Since these needs are related to the resources, opportunities, conditions, and problems in the environment, it is important that both the student body and the community be analyzed and described. The characteristics of the community served by a school system should be identified according to their current and emerging local uniqueness. The relationship of these characteristics to the responsibilities of the secondary school is a particular concern of this evaluation.

This section is organized to facilitate such analyses and descriptions. The goal is to describe the student body, the parents and the community as well as all available educational and cultural opportunities.

Information compiled in this section will be used with all other sections to assist in determining whether or not the educational program offered by the school meets the needs of the secondary school students of the community. If the data requested are already available in a format other than that suggested in this section it should be used. The school should also include, if available, additional data that describe the school although it is not specifically requested.

In preparing data for this section, it is imperative to keep in mind that in a school for secondary students one primary goal is the acquisition of general education and ways of acquiring knowledge. To be effective, the school program must be organized so that learning at this level is articulated with that offered at the junior high/middle school and with that offered at higher educational levels. The program also must take into account the nature of the community and its population in order to develop appropriate exploratory educational experiences for students. Another equally important goal is to involve students who are not college bound in learning experiences that help them make career choices, prepare them for careers or prepare them for further education in vocational-technical schools or trade schools. Ultimately, the school program must provide all students a sufficient background of experiences to make successful choices in their later school and life careers.

The descriptive analysis of the school and the community developed under the guidelines of this section is a necessary first step to obtain information that can serve as a foundation for program planning and evaluation.

I. The Students in the School

The characteristics of students as individuals, as subgroups and as a community group will help determine what programs and learning experiences are needed. School programs should be designed to provide both developmental and remedial opportunities for improved learning. A dynamic program should promote the progress of students of various abilities, aspirations and goals as well as adapt to the changing character of the school population.

A. Student Enrollment

1. Complete the chart below, using enrollments as of October 1 (approximately).
2. If the school is ungraded, use reasonable equivalents.

ENROLLMENT BY YEARS

GRADES INCLUDED IN THIS SCHOOL	PAST		PRESENT	PROJECTED	
	Three Years Ago 19____19____	One Year Ago 19____19____	This Year 19____19____	Next Year 19____19____	Three Years Hence 19____19____
	Number	Number	Number	Number	Number
Grade_____					
Grade_____					
Grade_____					
Grade_____					
Grade_____					
Grade_____					
Exceptional Students					
Total					

3. Explain any unusual variations in enrollments.

4. Services for Students with Exceptional Needs.

Check those blocks indicating how the different types of exceptional students are served in your school or served by another nearby school on a contractual arrangement. (More than one block may be checked; leave blank any type not being served.)

Classification	Special Education Service			Other Services	Number of F.T.E. Staff	Number of Students
	Special Class	Resource Room	Itinerant Teacher			
Educable mentally retarded				School psychologist		
Trainable mentally retarded				School social worker		
Learning disabled				Prevocational counseling and work-study program		
Socially maladjusted				Speech correction		
Emotionally disturbed				Vision screening		
Blind				Hearing screening		
Partially sighted				Physical therapy		
Deaf				Occupational therapy		
Hard of hearing				Mobility training		
Physically handicapped				Home instruction		
Multiple handicapped				Special tutoring		
Gifted				Special transportation		

B. Stability of Student Population

1. In the space below, indicate the number of years that each member of the highest grade has been in *this* school.

NUMBER OF YEARS IN THIS SCHOOL (INCLUDING PRESENT YEAR)	MEMBERS OF HIGHEST GRADE			
			Total	
	Boys	Girls	Number	Percent
1				
2				
3				
4				
5 or more				
Total				

2. Discuss any unusual conditions revealed by these tables.

C. Age-Grade Distribution
School Year for Which Data Are Given: 19_____-19_____

Indicate the number of pupils at each age level on October 1. (If the school is ungraded, estimate equivalents.)

GRADE	AGE								
	11	12	13	14	15	16	17	18	19 or Over
Grade_____									
Grade_____									
Grade_____									
Grade_____									
Grade_____									
Grade_____									
Exceptional Children									
Total									

1. If there is unusual variance in age-grade distribution of students:
   a. What factors exist within the feeder schools that may explain these unusual variations in distribution?

   b. Are there factors within the community (such as ethnic groups, socioeconomic conditions, labor surpluses, migrant and seasonal populations, first generation Americans, industrial exodus, automation, non-English speaking clusters) that may explain abnormalities in the age-grade distribution as indicated above?

D. Achievement

1. In the table below, indicate the percentage of boys and girls in each category or grade. If more appropriate (particularly at the high school level), use own data reporting forms.

Reading Achievement Norms													Grade 7 Percent		Grade 8 Percent		Grade 9 Percent		Grade 10 Percent		Grade 11 Percent		Grade 12 Percent		Total School Percent	
	Boys	Girls	Boys	Girls	Boys	Girls	Boys	Girls	Boys	Girls	Boys	Girls	Boys	Girls	Boys	Girls	Boys	Girls	Boys	Girls	Boys	Girls	Boys	Girls	Boys	Girls

2. Test(s) used in collecting data.

E. Student Characteristics

1. Describe any special characteristics with respect to artistic, musical or athletic skills.

2. Describe any special characteristics with respect to the physical, emotional and socioeconomic background of students. (Include handicap and disability information.)

F. Ethnic Characteristics of Student Body

1. List below the identifiable ethnic groups that compose the student body.

GROUP	Percent of Student Body NOW	Percent of Student Body 5 YEARS AGO
1		
2		
3		
4		
5		
6		
7		
8		
Total	100.0	100.0

2. Describe significant ethnic trends that have had or will have an impact on the school's educational program.

G. Education Intentions

1. Indicate the number and percent of members of the present senior class whose intentions are as follows:

Intentions	Boys	Girls	TOTAL	
			Number	Percent
Attend 4-year college or university				
Attend junior or community college				
Attend other post-secondary school, e.g., business college or technical institute				
Continue education but undecided on type of school				
Stop formal education upon graduation				
Undecided about further education				
Unknown				
Total members of senior class				

H. Follow-up Data of Graduates (Class of 19_____)

1. Indicate in the appropriate columns the number and percentage of graduates of the last senior class who have entered the educational and occupational categories:

CATEGORIES	Boys	Girls	TOTAL Number	TOTAL Percent
Attend 4-year college or university				
Attend junior or community college				
Attend other postsecondary school, e.g., business college or technical institute				
Occupation:				
Married				
Unemployed				
Unknown				
Total				

I. Withdrawals

1. In the table below, indicate the number of students who withdrew because of the reasons listed. Individual investigations should be made when possible. In other cases accept the reason given by the student. These data should represent a 12-month period (October 1–October 1) in order to include students who finish a term and fail to return the following term.

REASON FOR WITHDRAWAL	Boys	Girls	TOTAL	
			Number	Percent of Total Enrollment of School
State Reasons for Withdrawal				
Family financial difficulties				
Personal problems				
Academic problems				
Discipline problems				
Transfer to another school:				
Change in residence				
Student dissatisfaction				
Parental dissatisfaction				
Transportation problems				
Total Withdrawn				

2. In this table give the current status of those listed in the previous table.

Current Status	Boys	Girls	Total
Employed			
Military Service			
Apprenticeship			
Marriage			
Unemployed			
Unknown			
In school elsewhere			
Totals			

3. Discuss any unusual conditions revealed by these data.

4. What factors within the school or community contribute to these conditions.

J. Information Regarding Students' Parents

1. *Occupational status (Give percentage):**

Occupation	Father	Mother	Occupation	Father	Mother
Agricultural			Semiskilled		
Clerical			Service occupations		
Homemaker			Skilled		
Managerial			Unskilled		
Military			Unemployed		
Professional					

2. *Educational status of adults (count each parent only once):**

　　a) Percent of parents with formal education in elementary school only . . . . _____%

　　b) Percent of parents with partial but incomplete high school attendance . . . . _____%

　　c) Percent of parents who have completed high school . . . . _____%

　　d) Percent of parents with some formal education beyond high school other than college . . . . _____%

　　e) Percent of parents with some college education but without a degree . . . . _____%

　　f) Percent of parents with a bachelor's (or baccalaureate) degree . . . . _____%

　　g) Percent of parents with advanced degrees . . . . _____%

　　　　*These need not be the exact categories used.

3. *Percentage of the student body living in a two-parent household* . . . . _____%

K. Summary

1. Based on the information presented in this subsection and any other data considered pertinent, what significant generalizations can be made regarding the nature and needs of the student population?

2. These generalizations have implications relative to the school's statement of philosophy and objectives and the educational program designed to accomplish these objectives. Delineate these implications.

II. The School District

The quality of the educational program is frequently a function of the resources available and the number of students to be served. The following items deal with these important aspects of the school district.

A. Population and Enrollment Data

1. Total population . . . . ._____

2. Grade and enrollment distribution:

	Elementary Schools	Junior High/ Middle Schools	Senior High Schools
Grades included at each level:			
Public schools	_____	_____	_____
Nonpublic schools.	_____	_____	_____
Total enrollment at each level:			
Public schools	_____	_____	_____
Nonpublic schools.	_____	_____	_____

B. Financial Resources and Budgeting

Public Schools

1. Assessed valuation of the district . . . .$_____

   (Indicate the relationship of assessed value to actual value:_____%)

2. Tax rate per thousand dollars of assessed valuation . . . .$_____

3. Percent of local taxes appropriated for schools. . . . . ._____%

4. Total school district budget . . . .$_____

5. Percent of total budget derived from local sources . . . . ._____%

6. Cost per student: Elementary . . . .$_____

   Junior high school/middle school . . . .$_____

   High school . . . .$_____

7. Number of teachers (K-12). . . . . ._____

8. Attach a copy of the school district's salary schedule(s). Indicate the number of employees currently at each salary level.

9. Indicate what percent of the school district's budget is allotted to each major area (such as administration, instruction, transportation, supplies, equipment and maintenance).

C. Government and Foundation-Supported Programs

1. Describe any projects currently in operation in this school that are financed by federal, state or municipal agencies.

2. Describe any projects currently in operation in this school that are supported by philanthropic agencies or business organizations.

3. Describe how the facilities of the community and/or people in the community are used in any of these programs.

D. Summary

1. Based on the information presented in this subsection and any other data considered pertinent, what significant generalizations can be made regarding the resources available to the school?

2. These generalizations have implications relative to the school's statement of philosophy and the educational program designed to accomplish these objectives. Delineate these implications.

III. The Community

The accumulation and analysis of data about the community are logical steps in the evaluation of the school's program. A dynamic program will be sensitive to community needs and will focus on positive steps toward the solution of community education problems.

A. Describe important characteristics of the community that relate to the school and its programs and that have not been described in the foregoing pages. Explain how these characteristics have been responsible for the development of school programs and describe the programs. (Characteristics may include such matters as ethnic and racial groups, socioeconomic conditions, labor surpluses, migrant and seasonal residents, first-generation Americans, non-English language groups, industrial exodus, automation, declining employment opportunities, religious beliefs, subcultural folkways, biases and prejudices and public and private multiple-dwelling housing.)

B. Describe the following nonschool programs and/or facilities that are available and discuss (1) their adequacy, (2) any unique services that they offer to the students and the community and (3) the extent to which students use them:

1. Library facilities

2. Recreational opportunities and facilities

3. Parks

4. Choral and instrumental music organizations and programs

5. Dramatics organizations and programs

6. Arts and crafts programs

7. Museums, art galleries and zoos

8. Others (list)

C. List the major clubs and organizations in the community that are available to students (for example Scouts and 4-H).

D. Describe the post-high-school educational institutions that are available within the community:

1. Collegiate institutions

2. Vocational and technical schools

3. Institutions providing adult or continuing education

E. Discuss the extent to which school facilities are made available to the community after school hours.

F. Summary

1. Based on the information presented in this subsection and any other data considered pertinent, what significant generalizations can be made regarding the characteristics of the school community?

2. These generalizations have implications relative to the school's statement of philosophy and objectives and the educational program designed to accomplish these objectives. Delineate these implications.

IV. Climate of the School and Community

The general climate of the school and community exerts a profound influence on the school and its program. Every effort should be made to determine the quality of this climate.

A. The Student Climate

The *Student Opinion Inventory* developed and published by the National Study of School Evaluation or a similar valid instrument should be used to determine student attitude or opinions about the school, its administration, teachers and program. The *Evaluation Guidelines for Multicultural/Multiracial Education* developed and published by the National Study of School Evaluation also assesses attitudes of students and teachers about this important aspect of the educational program.

1. What are the significant findings of this study?

2. What are the implications?

B. The Faculty Climate

The *Teacher Opinion Inventory* developed by the National Study of School Evaluation or a similar valid instrument may be used to determine faculty attitudes or opinions concerning the school, its administration and program. Place the results in tabular form.

1. What are the significant findings of the study?

2. What are the implications?

C. The Community Climate

Important to the success of a school program is the attitude of the community toward the school and its program. The *Parent Opinion Inventory* developed by the National Study of School Evaluation or a similar valid instrument may be used to assess parents' attitudes. A cross-section of the public can be chosen if care is used to ensure that all groups are represented. Place findings in tabular form.

1. What are the significant findings of the study?

2. What are the implications?

D. Summary

1. What are the significant differences in the beliefs, attitudes or concepts of the three groups?

2. How can these be resolved?

School and Community
(Nonpublic Schools)

NAME OF SCHOOL_____

DATE_____

Prepared by

_____   _____

_____   _____

_____   _____

The committee given the responsibility for completing this section will find it beneficial to become thoroughly familiar with the entire section before attempting to react or respond to any part of it.

This section, "School and Community (Nonpublic Schools)," provides basic data for the complete evaluation. It is not to be completed by public schools. The importance of careful and accurate gathering of data cannot be overemphasized. This section should be completed before work is started on the other sections.

Although space has been provided throughout the section for committee responses, statements need not be limited to that space; the committee should feel free to attach addenda for items whose clarity will be improved by fuller development.

The completed report of this committee should be presented to the entire faculty for approval or modification.

NATIONAL STUDY OF SCHOOL EVALUATION
5201 Leesburg Pike, Falls Church, Virginia 22041

Organization of the Criteria

The *Secondary School Evaluative Criteria: Narrative Edition* (Revised) is composed of fourteen sections as follows:

M	Manual
N1	School and Community (Public Schools)
N2	School and Community (Nonpublic Schools)
O	Phliosophy and Objectives
P	Design of Curriculum
Q	Instructional Areas
R	Individual Faculty Data
S	School Staff and Administration
T	Learning Media Services
U	Guidance Services
V	Auxiliary Services
W	Student Activities Program
X	School Plant and Facilities
Y	Plans and Priorities

The "Manual" provides an overview of the evaluation process and explains in some detail how the materials may be used. The section on "School and Community" together with the section on "Philosophy and Objectives" form the foundation for the process and undergird the entire evaluation.

"School and Community" is a data-gathering section. The section "School and Community (Nonpublic Schools)" is designed specifically for use by independent, church-related and other nonpublic schools. "Philosophy and Objectives" is designed to assist in developing or reexamining the school's existing philosophy and objectives in light of the data provided by the "School and Community" section.

The next two sections, "Design of Curriculum" and "Instructional Areas," are also closely related. "Design of Curriculum" focuses on the organization of the curriculum. It is extremely important that the subcommittee completing this section is a representative body of the total school program. The "Instructional Areas" section makes possible the evaluation of each of the areas of learning that the school identifies.

The section on "Individual Faculty Data" includes data concerning individual faculty members and provides opportunity for those persons to express opinions on certain aspects of the school program. This is the only section that each faculty member completes individually. The "School Staff and Administration" section gives attention to administration, instructional staff and auxiliary staff. The "Learning Media Services" section includes media services, library and audio-visual services. The "Guidance Services" section includes information about personal, educational and career counseling and the guidance program. The section entitled "Auxiliary Services" examines such services as those dealing with health, food and transportation. The "Student Activities Program" section focuses on the school's total activities program. The next section deals with the school plant and facilities. The final section, "Plans and Priorities," provides an opportunity to place in priority the school's plans for improvement.

The sections P, Q, S, T, U, V, W, and X use this common format:

    I. Principles
    II. Description
    III. Evaluation
    IV. Plans for Improvement
    V. Current Status Scale

This five-point format begins with Part I, a series of principles designed to stimulate thought and reflection about the school program. Part II consists of probing questions designed to elicit a description of the program or area under consideration. Part III provides an opportunity to appraise and evaluate the program described in the second part and Part IV asks for the school's plans for improvement. Part V gives the school an opportunity to indicate its status in comparison to an "optimum" program.

The School's Task in Evaluation

The complete evaluation of a school as recommended by the National Study of School Evaluation is a three-step process. The first step is a self-evaluation carried out by the faculty of the individual school. This step usually requires a minimum of one year. The second step is an evaluation by a visiting committee, which usually requires a minimum of three days. The third step is the school's consideration and follow-up of the findings of the evaluation.

The National Study of School Evaluation has developed a means for recognizing that schools which are quite different may be equally sound educationally. This concept involves the basic principle that a school shall be evaluated in terms of what it is striving to accomplish (its philosophy and objectives) and according to the extent to which it is meeting the needs of the students who are enrolled or for whom it is responsible. The philosophy and objectives of the school must be acceptable to some agency (a community, an accrediting association, a state department of education) if the evaluation is to be recognized beyond the confines of the school.

School staff and administration, parents, students and members of the governing body should be actively involved in this self-evaluation. It is important that all who are involved understand that the purpose of this self-study is to improve the quality of the school's program through the means of self-evaluation and comprehensive examination of what is happening to students in the school environment.

It is important to recognize that no one section of the self-study is meant to stand alone. Each section has been designed to correlate with other sections to form a comprehensive self-evaluation. It is important that participants not become single-minded when working on a particular section and overlook the fact that the total evaluation does not rest on that particular section. Staff interaction is essential in bringing about change.

This instrument is designed for a wide variety of secondary schools. Therefore, some items may not be applicable to a particular school situation. Schools are reminded of their prerogative to strike or change words, so long as they do not misdirect the intent of a statement but render it more relevant. In the event that an entire statement appears to be irrelevant, a school may decide it does not apply and explain its view in the space provided.

Finally, it is vital that each evaluation participant receives feedback on reports of all sections of the self-study and that each participant have an opportunity to express either agreement or disagreement with each report. Provision should be made for modification of a report when advisable.

More detailed information may be found in the "Manual," Section M.

Statement of Purpose

The evaluation of a school must, to a large extent, be based on the degree to which its educational program meets the needs of the students, the parents and the larger community. Since these needs are related to the resources, opportunities and conditions in the community, it is important that analyses be made and described.

This section is organized to present such information. The goal is to describe the student body, the parents and the community as well as all available educational and cultural opportunities. Information compiled here will serve as a guide in all other sections of the instrument to assist in determining the degree to which the school program serves the students, parents and community.

I. Students in the School

The characteristics of the student body will help determine what programs and learning experiences are needed. School programs should be designed to provide both developmental and remedial opportunities for improved learning.

A dynamic program should promote the progress of students of various abilities, aspirations and goals as well as be adaptable to the changing character of the school population.

A. Student Enrollment

1. Complete the chart below, using enrollments as of October 1 (approximately).

2. If the school is ungraded, use reasonable equivalents.

ENROLLMENT BY YEARS

GRADES INCLUDED IN THIS SCHOOL	PAST		PRESENT	PROJECTED	
	Three Years Ago 19____ 19____	One Year Ago 19____ 19____	This Year 19____ 19____	Next Year 19____ 19____	Three Years Hence 19____ 19____
	Number	Number	Number	Number	Number
Grade _____					
Grade _____					
Grade _____					
Grade _____					
Grade _____					
Grade _____					
Exceptional Students					
Total					

3. Explain any unusual variations in enrollments.

4. Complete the chart in regard to projected enrollment for your school.

B. Stability of Student Population

1. In the space below, indicate the number of years that each member of the highest grade has been in *this* school.

NUMBER OF YEARS IN THIS SCHOOL (INCLUDING PRESENT YEAR)	MEMBERS OF HIGHEST GRADE			
	Boys	Girls	Total Number	Total Percent
1				
2				
3				
4				
5 or more				
Total				

2. Discuss any unusual conditions revealed by these tables.

C. Age-Grade Distribution

School Year for Which Data Are Given: 19____ – 19____

Indicate the number of pupils at each age level on October 1. (If the school is ungraded, estimate equivalents.)

GRADE	AGE						
	11	12	13	14	15	16	17 or Over
Grade _____							
Grade _____							
Grade _____							
Grade _____							
Grade _____							
Grade _____							
Exceptional Children							
Total							

D. Mental Ability

1. If intelligence or mental ability test records are available, give number of students who score in each of the following IQ or percentile ranges. In case the school does not have data suitable for this table, give equivalent distribution either in this form, revised as necessary, or on a separate sheet. If neither request can be met, describe briefly the general mental ability of pupils. A school may modify the intervals listed below to agree with data already available.

RANGE*		Grade _____	Grade _____	Grade _____	Grade _____	Grade _____	Grade _____	TOTAL	
IQ	Percentile							Number	%
Over 124	Over 94								
117–124	85–94								
109–116	70–84								
92–108	31–69								
84–91	16–30								
76–83	6–15								
Below 76	Below 6								
Total									
Year in which tests were given									

*Indicate which column is being used by circling "IQ" or "Percentile."

2. List test(s) used in collecting data.

E. Achievement

1. In the table below, indicate the percentage of boys and girls in each category or grade. If more appropriate (particularly at the high school level), use own data-reporting forms.

Reading Achievement Norms	Grade ____ Percent		Grade ____ Percent		Grade ____ Percent		Grade ____ Percent		Grade ____ Percent		Grade ____ Percent		Grade ____ Percent		Total School Percent	
	Boys	Girls	Boys	Girls	Boys	Girls	Boys	Girls	Boys	Girls	Boys	Girls	Boys	Girls	Boys	Girls
4 or more years above																
3 years above																
2 years above																
1 year above																
At Grade Level																
1 year below																
2 years below																
3 years below																
4 years below																

2. Test(s) used in collecting data.

In the table below, indicate the names and dates of the administration of mathematics tests for each grade.

	Name(s) of Test(s)	Date(s) of Test(s)
Grade _____		
Grade _____		
Grade _____		
Grade _____		
Grade _____		
Grade _____		
Grade _____		

What test or tests were used in determining these data? Indicate the grade level at which each test was given and the name of the test used.

Grade Level	Name of Test
Grade _____	
Grade _____	
Grade _____	
Grade _____	
Grade _____	
Grade _____	
Grade _____	

F. Ethnic Characteristics

1. List below the identifiable ethnic groups that comprise the student body. (An ethnic group is defined as a group with a common cultural tradition and a sense of identity which exists as a subgroup of a larger society).

GROUP	Percent of Student Body Now	Percent of Student Body 5 Years Ago
TOTAL	100.00	100.00

2. Describe significant changes in the ethnic composition of the student body in recent years.

G. Educational Intentions

Indicate the number and percent of members of the present senior class whose intentions are as follows:

Intentions	Boys	Girls	TOTAL	
			Number	Percent
Attend 4-year college or university				
Attend junior or community college				
Attend other post-secondary school, e.g., business college or technical institute				
Continue education but undecided on type of school				
Stop formal education upon graduation				
Undecided about further education				
Unknown				
Total members of senior class				

H. Follow-up Data of Graduates (Class of 19____)

Indicate in the appropriate columns the number and percentage of graduates of the last senior class who have entered the educational and occupational categories:

CATEGORIES	Boys	Girls	TOTAL	
			Number	Percent
Attend 4-year college or university				
Attend junior or community college				
Attend other post-secondary school, e.g., business college or technical institute				
Occupation:				
Planned delay of further schooling				
Military Service				
Married				
Unemployed				
Unknown				
Total				

I. Withdrawals

1. In the table below indicate the major reason for withdrawal given by each pupil. If no major reason was given, determine the most plausible reason from the records of the pupil. Do not count any pupil more than once. Include those who have withdrawn from school during the 12 months preceding the opening of the current school year.

| Reason for Withdrawal | Number Withdrawn at Each Grade or Level | | | | | | | Number | | Total for Each Reason |
	Grade ___	Grade ___	Grade ___	Grade ___	Grade ___	Grade ___	Grade ___	Boys	Girls	
Change of Residence										
Change of school										
Financial problems										
Transportation problem										
Personal problem										
Academic difficulty										
Discipline problem										
Pupil dissatisfaction										
Parental dissatisfaction										
Other										
	TOTAL									

2. Does any pattern emerge (e.g., academic difficulty in the upper grades, pupil dissatisfaction more predominent among girls, etc.)? If so, discuss.

3. Indicate the type of school to which the pupils transferred:

Type	Number
Public	
Church-related	
Independent	
Other Nonpublic	
	TOTAL

J. Information regarding Students' Parents

1. Occupational status (give percentage):

Occupation	Father	Mother	Occupation	Father	Mother
Agricultural			Semiskilled		
Clerical			Service occupations		
			Skilled		
Managerial			Unskilled		
Military			Unemployed		
Professional			Other		

2. Educational status of adults (count each parent only once):*

   a) Percent of parents with formal education in elementary school only . . . . _____ %
   b) Percent of parents with partial but incomplete high school attendance . . . . _____ %
   c) Percent of parents who have completed high school . . . . _____ %
   d) Percent of parents with some formal education beyond high school other than college . . . . _____ %
   e) Percent of parents with some college education but without a degree . . . . _____ %
   f) Percent of parents with a bachelor's (or baccalaureate) degree . . . . _____ %
   g) Percent of parents with advanced degrees . . . . _____ %
     *These need not be the exact categories used.

3. Percent of the student body living in a two-parent household . . . . _____ %

K. Admissions and Recruitment

1. What qualities or characteristics attract pupils to your school?

2. Compare the present pupil enrollment with the school capacity.

3. Who is responsible for recruitment and admissions?

4. Briefly list the admissions policies, criteria and procedures for admitting pupils to the school.

5. Describe the recruitment program, including elements such as brochures, newspaper, radio, TV, special activities and community groups. When practical, attach materials. In other cases (e.g., slide shows), describe the items in detail and indicate where they may be examined.

6. What scholarships or student aid funds are available? Describe the criteria used for distribution of scholarship assistance.

7. What outside individuals or groups are used to assist admission and recruitment efforts?

8. What changes should be incorporated into your admissions and recruitment programs?

9. List short-term and long-term plans to implement needed changes in admissions and recruitment programs.

II. Community

A. Background Information

Summarize the history and major characteristics of the community, the school and the student body.

B. Members of the Community

1. Define the groups that constitute the school community (e.g., alumni, church, parents, grandparents and other patrons of the school.)

2. Briefly describe the manner and frequency of relating to each group.

C. Public Relations

1. Who is responsible for public relations materials and activities?

2. Describe the public relations program. Where practical, attach materials. In other cases (e.g., slide shows, scrapbooks of newspaper articles), describe the items in detail and indicate where they may be examined.

D. Facilities and Programs

1. Describe facilities and programs outside the school (libraries, museums, theaters, arts programs, sports events, etc.) that are available for student use. Specify the manner and extent of usage within the past academic year as well as any future plans for similar facilities or events.

Facility or Program	Usage in Past Academic Year	Future Plans For Use

2. Describe the manner and extent to which school facilities are made available to the community.

E. Organizations and Individuals

1. List organizations and individuals who regularly provide learning experiences or other service to the school:

Organizations/Individuals	Type and Frequency of Service

2. List ways in which pupils regularly offer service to groups or individuals outside of the school:

Groups/Individuals	Type and Frequency of Service

F. Other Schools

1. List the other schools (nonpublic and public) with which you are coordinating activities or endeavors. Describe all present and planned activities and endeavors.

2. List the high schools/colleges that graduates most frequently attend. Describe all present and planned articulation efforts.

III. School Finance

A. Financial Structure and Support Data

1. List sources of income according to percentages of total (use data from last audit).

Source	Percentage
a. Tuition	
b. Fees	
c. Revenue special activities programs	
d. Interest/revenue general operating fund	
e. Foundations	
f. Annual giving	
g. Capital giving	
h. Endowments	
i. Memorials	
j. Subsidies	
k. Sundry/charitable contributions	
l. Other	

2. Aside from the revenue from tuition and fees, indicate the amount of yearly support for the annual operating budget and for the capital projects of the school.

3. If available, indicate the amount of the annual support from:

a. Present parents	
b. Alumni, parents, grandparents and other patrons of the school	

4. Indicate the yearly cost per student, using the formula $\dfrac{\text{Operating expenditures}}{\text{Number of students}}$

    $ _____

5. Describe and attach your tuition and fee schedule.

6. Indicate the total number of full-time_____ and part-time teachers_____ in the school.

7. Attach a copy of the school's salary schedule or ranges.

8. Describe in detail the fringe benefits offered to the faculty and staff.

9. Describe the financial accounting system used by the school; (i.e., fund accounting, zero-based budgeting, parish or diocesan arrangement, profit/loss statements, outside or independent audits, other). Attach a copy of your annual operating budget and latest financial statement (optional).

10. Describe provisions for the accounting and management of endowment funds and/or the results of fund-raising efforts.

B. Budget Planning

1. Describe the budget planning process used in the school.

2. Describe the nature of the school staff's participation in the preparation of the school's annual budget.

3. Describe what, if any, community involvement or participation takes place in developing the school's annual budget.

C. Government and Foundation-Supported Programs

1. Describe any projects currently in operation in this school that are financed by federal, state or municipal agencies.

2. Describe any projects currently in operation in this school that are supported by philanthropic agencies or business organizations.

3. Describe any programs currently in operation in this school that are supported by the joint efforts of several schools (e.g., collective or cooperative purchasing, shared use of school facilities, materials or faculty).

4. Describe how community facilities and/or people in the community are involved in any of these programs.

D. Other Pertinent Special Data

Due to the uniqueness of independent, church-related and other nonpublic schools, there may be other relevant data dealing with the finances of a school when reviewing the overall fiscal status. If such is the case with your school situation, please describe in detail. (Note: The balance of this section should not be completed until the end of the self-study.)

1. Describe your school's major strengths related to your present financial situation.

2. Describe your school's major weaknesses related to your present financial situation.

3. What procedures have been developed to carry on a continuous evaluation of this school area?

IV. Climate of the School and Community

The general climate of the school and community exerts a profound influence on the school and its program. Every effort should be made to determine the quality of this climate.

A. The Student Climate

The *Student Opinion Inventory* developed and published by the National Study of School Evaluation or a similar valid instrument may be used to determine student attitudes or opinions about the school, its administration, teachers and program. The *Evaluation Guidelines for Multicultural/Multiracial Education* published by the National Study of School Evaluation also assesses attitudes of students and teachers about this important aspect of the educational program.

1. What are the significant findings of this study?

2. What are the implications?

B. The Faculty Climate

The *Teacher Opinion Inventory* developed by the National Study of School Evaluation or a similar valid instrument may be used to determine faculty attitudes or opinions concerning the school, its administration and program. Place the results in tabular form.

1. What are the significant findings of the study?

2. What are the implications?

C. The Community Climate

Important to the success of a school program is the attitude of the community toward the school and its program. The *Parent Opinion Inventory* developed by the National Study of School Evaluation or a similar valid instrument may be used to assess parent attitudes. A cross-section of the public can be chosen if care is used to ensure that all groups are represented. Place the findings in tabular form.

1. What are the significant findings of the study?

2. What are the implications?

D. Summary

1. What are the significant differences in the beliefs, attitudes or concepts of the three groups?

2. How can these differences be resolved?

Philosophy and Objectives

NAME OF SCHOOL_____

DATE_____

Prepared by

_____   _____

_____   _____

_____

    The committee completing this section will find it beneficial to become thoroughly familiar with the entire section before attempting to react or respond to any part of it.

    The "Philosophy and Objectives" section is one of the basic sections upon which the evaluation rests. One of the fundamental principles of evaluation that the National Study of School Evaluation supports is that a school should be evaluated in terms of what it is striving to accomplish. This section is unique in the self-study/evaluation process in two primary respects: it establishes the essential frame of reference for evaluations and decision making and it commands the active involvement of all participant groups—faculty and staff, students and parents, representatives of administration, the governing board and the community. In addition, this uniqueness is reflected in the essential function of the committee having responsibility. Rather than completing an assignment and then reporting to the entire faculty and others, this committee is charged with providing leadership and assistance in a cooperative process of either development or review and revision. The committee should develop the school's philosophy and objectives or reexamine its existent philosophy and objectives in light of the institution's mission as defined by the governing board or sponsoring group, the data provided by the "School and Community" section, and the basic beliefs of the staff, students and community.

    The words "philosophy" and "objective" as used in this instrument will be defined as:

    Philosophy: A statement of examined beliefs that provides a source of direction in determining the school's educational objectives.

    Objective: A guideline expressed in practical terms for the selection of programs to implement the philosophy.

    Although space has been provided throughout the section for committee responses, statements need not be limited to that space; the committee should feel free to attach addenda for items so that clarity will be improved by fuller development.

    It is especially important that the report of this committee be presented to the faculty and administration for approval or modification before beginning on the remainder of the study inasmuch as understanding and acceptance by all involved is vital to a productive and effective evaluation.

NATIONAL STUDY OF SCHOOL EVALUATION
5201 Leesburg Pike, Falls Church, Virginia 22041

Organization of the Criteria

The *Secondary School Evaluative Criteria: Narrative Edition* (Revised) is composed of fourteen sections as follows:

M	Manual
N1	School and Community (Public Schools)
N2	School and Community (Nonpublic Schools)
O	Phliosophy and Objectives
P	Design of Curriculum
Q	Instructional Areas
R	Individual Faculty Data
S	School Staff and Administration
T	Learning Media Services
U	Guidance Services
V	Auxiliary Services
W	Student Activities Program
X	School Plant and Facilities
Y	Plans and Priorities

The "Manual" provides an overview of the evaluation process and explains in some detail how the materials may be used. The section on "School and Community" together with the section on "Philosophy and Objectives" form the foundation for the process and undergird the entire evaluation.

"School and Community" is a data-gathering section. The section "School and Community (Nonpublic Schools)" is designed specifically for use by independent, church-related and other nonpublic schools. "Philosophy and Objectives" is designed to assist in developing or reexamining the school's existing philosophy and objectives in light of the data provided by the "School and Community" section.

The next two sections, "Design of Curriculum" and "Instructional Areas," are also closely related. "Design of Curriculum" focuses on the organization of the curriculum. It is extremely important that the subcommittee completing this section is a representative body of the total school program. The "Instructional Areas" section makes possible the evaluation of each of the areas of learning that the school identifies.

The section on "Individual Faculty Data" includes data concerning individual faculty members and provides opportunity for those persons to express opinions on certain aspects of the school program. This is the only section that each faculty member completes individually. The "School Staff and Administration" section gives attention to administration, instructional staff and auxiliary staff. The "Learning Media Services" section includes media services, library and audio-visual services. The "Guidance Services" section includes information about personal, educational and career counseling and the guidance program. The section entitled "Auxiliary Services" examines such services as those dealing with health, food and transportation. The "Student Activities Program" section focuses on the school's total activities program. The next section deals with the school plant and facilities. The final section, "Plans and Priorities," provides an opportunity to place in priority the school's plans for improvement.

The sections P, Q, S, T, U, V, W, and X use this common format:

I. Principles
II. Description
III. Evaluation
IV. Plans for Improvement
V. Current Status Scale

This five-point format begins with Part I, a series of principles designed to stimulate thought and reflection about the school program. Part II consists of probing questions designed to elicit a description of the program or area under consideration. Part III provides an opportunity to appraise and evaluate the program described in the second part and Part IV asks for the school's plans for improvement. Part V gives the school an opportunity to indicate its status in comparison to an "optimum" program.

The School's Task in Evaluation

The complete evaluation of a school as recommended by the National Study of School Evaluation is a three-step process. The first step is a self-evaluation carried out by the faculty of the individual school. This step usually requires a minimum of one year. The second step is an evaluation by a visiting committee, which usually requires a minimum of three days. The third step is the school's consideration and follow-up of the findings of the evaluation.

The National Study of School Evaluation has developed a means for recognizing that schools which are quite different may be equally sound educationally. This concept involves the basic principle that a school shall be evaluated in terms of what it is striving to accomplish (its philosophy and objectives) and according to the extent to which it is meeting the needs of the students who are enrolled or for whom it is responsible. The philosophy and objectives of the school must be acceptable to some agency (a community, an accrediting association, a state department of education) if the evaluation is to be recognized beyond the confines of the school.

School staff and administration, parents, students and members of the governing body should be actively involved in this self-evaluation. It is important that all who are involved understand that the purpose of this self-study is to improve the quality of the school's program through the means of self-evaluation and comprehensive examination of what is happening to students in the school environment.

It is important to recognize that no one section of the self-study is meant to stand alone. Each section has been designed to correlate with other sections to form a comprehensive self-evaluation. It is important that participants not become single-minded when working on a particular section and overlook the fact that the total evaluation does not rest on that particular section. Staff interaction is essential in bringing about change.

This instrument is designed for a wide variety of secondary schools. Therefore, some items may not be applicable to a particular school situation. Schools are reminded of their prerogative to strike or change words, so long as they do not misdirect the intent of a statement but render it more relevant. In the event that an entire statement appears to be irrelevant, a school may decide it does not apply and explain its view in the space provided.

Finally, it is vital that each evaluation participant receives feedback on reports of all sections of the self-study and that each participant have an opportunity to express either agreement or disagreement with each report. Provision should be made for modification of a report when advisable.

More detailed information may be found in the "Manual," Section M.

Overview

Each school should have a written statement of its philosophy and objectives consistent with the unique needs of the students it serves. This means that a statement of philosophy and objectives can neither be adopted nor adapted from that of any other school.

It should be noted here, however, that the statement of philosophy and objectives of a school that is part of a system should be consistent with the more general statement of philosophy and objectives of the system.

Because statements of philosophy and objectives are basic to the development of meaningful educational programs and the creation of an environment conducive to learning, it is important that each statement be arrived at through the use of democratic processes reflecting the best thinking of the students, parents and the governing body.

Schools having a written statement of philosophy and objectives need to review such statements for current relevancy and to determine whether or not they are consistent with and define the needs and characteristics of students currently being served by the school.

Schools developing an initial statement of philosophy and objectives may find some of the following suggestions helpful. The formulation process might include three stages of development. The first would be one in which all participants would individually examine their beliefs concerning the overall purposes of education in our society, the role of the school in the educational process and the unique role of this particular school in light of the special individual needs of the pupils it serves.

The second stage would consist of a series of discussions focusing on desirable philosophy and objectives for this school. In this process complete agreement of all participants should not be anticipated because each individual brings to the discussion his own personal biases and beliefs. It is important that divergent views expressed by participants be heard and considered. It is also desirable that a consensus or majority viewpoint be arrived at prior to the conclusion of this step.

In the third stage, a committee of the participants should draft the statement of philosophy and objectives discussed by the group and submit it to them for modification or approval. At this point it may be desirable to submit the statement to the administration and governing board for approval.

A. Guiding Principles for a Statement of Philosophy

Every school needs a carefully formulated, comprehensive statement of philosophy. Such a statement serves as a basis for forming a judgment as to whether the school involved is in fact achieving its objectives. Through the process of self-study all phases of the entire school program are examined in order to determine if all aspects are carried out in accordance with the stated philosophy and objectives.

The following items may be helpful, but should not be limiting, in determining the content of the statement of philosophy.

1. Relevance of the statement of philosophy to the larger purposes of the American democratic commitment.
2. Attention to intellectual, democratic, moral and social values basic to satisfying the needs of the individual and his culture.
3. Recognition of individual differences.
4. The special characteristics and unique needs of students.
5. Concern for the nature of knowledge and for the nature of the learning process as they apply to learners and their total development.
6. Consistency of philosophy with actual practice.
7. Identification of the roles, relationships and responsibilities of the community, the students, the teachers, the administration and the governing body in the educational process of the school.
8. The responsibility for making a determination as to a desirable balance among activities designed to promote student growth and development in the cognitive, affective and psychomotor domains.
9. The relationship of the school to all other educational learning centers.
10. The role of the school with respect to social and economic change.
11. The accountability of the school to the community it serves.

Attach a copy of your school's statement of philosophy.

B. Guiding Principles for a Statement of Objectives

A school's philosophy and objectives are implemented in various ways—through the programs of instruction, co-curricular activities, special services, utilization of learning media, application of staff competencies, teaching strategies and a favorable climate for learning. Certain objectives, however, are of such overriding importance that they become a central commitment to all apsects of the educational program for students. Each staff member should accept responsibility for attaining these priorities in light of his or her specific professional assignment.

Examples of certain objectives which become educational commitments that a school might have are intellectual, personal, social, physical, moral, ethical, spiritual and aesthetical development.

These commitments can then become the major headings for the specific objectives that are compatible with the school's beliefs.

While the statement of philosophy expresses beliefs and values, the statement of objectives gives direction to the program through the identification of desired student outcomes.

The statement of objectives may be related to—but need not be limited to—the items listed below:

1. The general objectives of the school.
2. Desirable characteristics of the student's total educational environment.

3. Recognition and appreciation of sound learning theories which have been supported by research.
4. Respect for individual differences among students and ways of providing for these differences.
5. Recognition of the obligation to provide citizenship experiences necessary to function in a free American society.
6. Development of social and occupational awareness.
7. Physical, mental, emotional, moral and social maturation of the students in a rapidly changing culture.
8. Continuation of the development of essential learnings.
9. Recognition of the need to provide for research and innovation.
10. Provision for a wide range of exploratory and socializing experiences and activities for all students.
11. Student development to help students achieve a positive self-concept and recognize and accept their potentials and limitations.

Attach a copy of your school's statement of objectives.

C. What procedures were used in preparing the current statement of philosophy and objectives?
   (If surveys or opinionnaires were used in developing or updating the statement of philosophy and objectives, a copy with an analysis and summary should be included.)

D. In what ways do the statement of philosophy and objectives reflect known characteristics of the school and community?

E. What provisions have been made for keeping the school community informed about the school's philosophy and objectives?

F. What plans have been made for examining and updating the philosophy and objectives periodically or whenever a significant change in the nature of the student body, faculty or community occurs?

G. Comments (add any other comments concerning the philosophy and objectives):

Design of Curriculum

NAME OF SCHOOL_____

DATE_____

Prepared by

_____   _____

_____   _____

_____   _____

     The committee given the responsibility for completing this section will find it beneficial to become thoroughly familiar with the entire section before attempting to react or respond to any part of it. It should be noted that this section is especially related to Section Q, "Instructional Areas."

     The committee should recognize that Sections N and O titled "School and Community" and "Philosophy and Objectives" together form the foundation for the total evaluation. The responses in all other sections should reflect an awareness of the characteristics of both the school and the community and the influence of the statements of philosophy.

     Although space has been provided through the section for committee responses, statements need not be limited to that space; the committee should feel free to attach addenda for items whose clarity will be improved by fuller development.

     The report of this committee, when completed, should be presented to the entire faculty for approval or modification.

NATIONAL STUDY OF SCHOOL EVALUATION
5201 Leesburg Pike, Falls Church, Virginia 22041

Organization of the Criteria

The *Secondary School Evaluative Criteria: Narrative Edition* (Revised) is composed of fourteen sections as follows:

M	Manual
N1	School and Community (Public Schools)
N2	School and Community (Nonpublic Schools)
O	Phliosophy and Objectives
P	Design of Curriculum
Q	Instructional Areas
R	Individual Faculty Data
S	School Staff and Administration
T	Learning Media Services
U	Guidance Services
V	Auxiliary Services
W	Student Activities Program
X	School Plant and Facilities
Y	Plans and Priorities

The "Manual" provides an overview of the evaluation process and explains in some detail how the materials may be used. The section on "School and Community" together with the section on "Philosophy and Objectives" form the foundation for the process and undergird the entire evaluation.

"School and Community" is a data-gathering section. The section "School and Community (Nonpublic Schools)" is designed specifically for use by independent, church-related and other nonpublic schools. "Philosophy and Objectives" is designed to assist in developing or reexamining the school's existing philosophy and objectives in light of the data provided by the "School and Community" section.

The next two sections, "Design of Curriculum" and "Instructional Areas," are also closely related. "Design of Curriculum" focuses on the organization of the curriculum. It is extremely important that the subcommittee completing this section is a representative body of the total school program. The "Instructional Areas" section makes possible the evaluation of each of the areas of learning that the school identifies.

The section on "Individual Faculty Data" includes data concerning individual faculty members and provides opportunity for those persons to express opinions on certain aspects of the school program. This is the only section that each faculty member completes individually. The "School Staff and Administration" section gives attention to administration, instructional staff and auxiliary staff. The "Learning Media Services" section includes media services, library and audio-visual services. The "Guidance Services" section includes information about personal, educational and career counseling and the guidance program. The section entitled "Auxiliary Services" examines such services as those dealing with health, food and transportation. The "Student Activities Program" section focuses on the school's total activities program. The next section deals with the school plant and facilities. The final section, "Plans and Priorities," provides an opportunity to place in priority the school's plans for improvement.

The sections P, Q, S, T, U, V, W, and X use this common format:

    I. Principles
    II. Description
    III. Evaluation
    IV. Plans for Improvement
    V. Current Status Scale

This five-point format begins with Part I, a series of principles designed to stimulate thought and reflection about the school program. Part II consists of probing questions designed to elicit a description of the program or area under consideration. Part III provides an opportunity to appraise and evaluate the program described in the second part and Part IV asks for the school's plans for improvement. Part V gives the school an opportunity to indicate its status in comparison to an "optimum" program.

The School's Task in Evaluation

The complete evaluation of a school as recommended by the National Study of School Evaluation is a three-step process. The first step is a self-evaluation carried out by the faculty of the individual school. This step usually requires a minimum of one year. The second step is an evaluation by a visiting committee, which usually requires a minimum of three days. The third step is the school's consideration and follow-up of the findings of the evaluation.

The National Study of School Evaluation has developed a means for recognizing that schools which are quite different may be equally sound educationally. This concept involves the basic principle that a school shall be evaluated in terms of what it is striving to accomplish (its philosophy and objectives) and according to the extent to which it is meeting the needs of the students who are enrolled or for whom it is responsible. The philosophy and objectives of the school must be acceptable to some agency (a community, an accrediting association, a state department of education) if the evaluation is to be recognized beyond the confines of the school.

School staff and administration, parents, students and members of the governing body should be actively involved in this self-evaluation. It is important that all who are involved understand that the purpose of this self-study is to improve the quality of the school's program through the means of self-evaluation and comprehensive examination of what is happening to students in the school environment.

It is important to recognize that no one section of the self-study is meant to stand alone. Each section has been designed to correlate with other sections to form a comprehensive self-evaluation. It is important that participants not become single-minded when working on a particular section and overlook the fact that the total evaluation does not rest on that particular section. Staff interaction is essential in bringing about change.

This instrument is designed for a wide variety of secondary schools. Therefore, some items may not be applicable to a particular school situation. Schools are reminded of their prerogative to strike or change words, so long as they do not misdirect the intent of a statement but render it more relevant. In the event that an entire statement appears to be irrelevant, a school may decide it does not apply and explain its view in the space provided.

Finally, it is vital that each evaluation participant receives feedback on reports of all sections of the self-study and that each participant have an opportunity to express either agreement or disagreement with each report. Provision should be made for modification of a report when advisable.

More detailed information may be found in the "Manual," Section M.

I. Principles

Introduction

The optimum development of the secondary school student requires a curriculum which is characterized by unity, balance, flexibility and articulation with the educational units above and below it, within the school itself and with the society in which the student lives. Based upon what is known about high school students, the curriculum design must also take into account their concerns and problems, individual differences and their common needs as young adults and citizens in our society. Since learning experiences and programs may be organized in various ways, school personnel should examine alternative patterns they consider most appropriate and continually evaluate their effectiveness.

Listed below are a number of principles regarding curriculum design which are generally held to be valid and to which the school community should address itself. This introduction is designed to encourage introspection concerning this section of the self-study. It is a starting point for discussion and for interaction among participants preparatory to delving into the nature of this aspect of the school program. Participants should avoid lengthy debate over the adequacy or the inadequacy of each principle.

Rather, it is important that the committee assigned this responsibility react to each statement in terms of an overview of how the school community generally accepts and implements each principle.

Indicate by circling the appropriate number in the first column to the right of each principle the degree to which that principle is accepted by the school and indicate by circling the appropriate number in the second column the degree to which that principle is implemented in the school. Where necessary, in order to be consistent with your stated philosophy and objectives, principles may be modified and added.

The descriptions of the numbers listed immediately below apply to the numbers in the columns to the right of the principles and should be borne in mind when marking the degree of acceptance and the degree of implementation.

Degree of Acceptance

1. Unacceptable
2. Questionable
3. Accept with reservations
4. Accept in general
5. Endorse completely

Degree of Implementation

1. Not implemented
2. Weakly implemented
3. Moderately implemented
4. Strongly implemented
5. Fully implemented

Principles

The design of the curriculum:

	Degree Acceptance	Degree Implementation
1. Is based upon realistic objectives specifically designed for the school and community it serves	1 2 3 4 5	1 2 3 4 5
2. Is based upon an assessment of student characterisics which affect the attainment of the school's goals and objectives	1 2 3 4 5	1 2 3 4 5
3. Is characterized by unity: all parts contribute to the achievement of the school's philosophy and objectives	1 2 3 4 5	1 2 3 4 5
4. Is characterized by balance: emphasis given to any instructional area or program element is proportionate to its importance in the achievement of the school's objectives	1 2 3 4 5	1 2 3 4 5
5. Is characterized by articulation: learning for students is free from gaps and unnecessary repetition:		
a. within instructional areas	1 2 3 4 5	1 2 3 4 5
b. between instructional areas	1 2 3 4 5	1 2 3 4 5
c. between the school and its feeder schools	1 2 3 4 5	1 2 3 4 5
d. between the school and post-high school education	1 2 3 4 5	1 2 3 4 5
e. between the school and the work world	1 2 3 4 5	1 2 3 4 5
6. Is characterized by flexibility:		
a. provides for individual differences among students	1 2 3 4 5	1 2 3 4 5
b. provides for program changes as students, parents, teachers and other staff members see the need	1 2 3 4 5	1 2 3 4 5
7. Provides for the essential learnings of all students	1 2 3 4 5	1 2 3 4 5
8. Recognizes that learning styles of individual students can and do differ markedly, that no one school can be best for all students and therefore provides alternative programs either within or without its own organizational structure	1 2 3 4 5	1 2 3 4 5
9. Affords students an opportunity to identify, examine and cope with current problems and issues of concern to them and to society in general	1 2 3 4 5	1 2 3 4 5

	Degree Acceptance					Degree Implementation				
10. Provides students with learning opportunities which foster the skills and attitudes necessary for self-directed learning and entrance into the job market	1	2	3	4	5	1	2	3	4	5
11. Provides for the special characteristics of the exceptional child (i.e., the gifted and the handicapped)	1	2	3	4	5	1	2	3	4	5
12. Recognizes the student activities program as an extension of the formal curriculum	1	2	3	4	5	1	2	3	4	5
13. Provides a system for continuous evaluation of the curriculum	1	2	3	4	5	1	2	3	4	5
14. Provides a system for continuous evaluation of instruction	1	2	3	4	5	1	2	3	4	5
15. Accommodates experimentation with new materials, procedures and programs	1	2	3	4	5	1	2	3	4	5
16. Uses local and other research findings as a basis for making curricular and instructional decisions	1	2	3	4	5	1	2	3	4	5

17. Others

II. Description of the Program

Following are a number of items regarding the overall design of the curriculum. Respond to each item and supply the supporting data specified.

A. Attach copies of the school's program of studies and schedule.

B. Explain the organization of the curriculum (e.g., required and elective courses, prerequisites, procedures for awarding credit, interdisciplinary articulation, etc.).

C. List the requirements for graduation.

D. Describe the means by which the all-school testing program is planned.

E. In what ways are the needs of individual students assessed and how does the design of the curriculum provide for these differing needs?

F. What procedures and related materials are used to guide students in selecting those portions of the curriculum most suited to their needs?

G. Explain how the staff is organized for instruction (e.g., departments, divisions, interdisciplinary teams, school within a school, etc.).

H. Describe the school's curriculum development procedures and how teachers, administrators, supervisors, guidance personnel, media specialists, students, parents and consultants are involved in the process.

I. What assurances are built into the curriculum development process that promote logical balance, scope and sequence?

J. How are follow-up studies and research data used in curriculum development?

K. Describe the extent to which time, facilities and financial support are provided for experimentation, innovation and evaluation in the development of the curriculum.

L. Explain how a balance is maintained in the curriculum 1) among programs designed for students' varying abilities and future goals, and 2) between learning experiences of an academic nature and those which are practical or co-curricular.

M. Describe any provisions that have been made, either within the school or external to the school, for alternative programs for those students whose interests or learning styles make the school's regular program inappropriate for them.

N. What efforts are made to ensure that the curriculum design provides adequate opportunity for students to gain experience in dealing with current problems and issues in our society? (e.g., racism, minority rights, environmental protection, the role of government, drug abuse, etc.)

O. In what ways does the curriculum aid students in identifying and preparing for post-high school goals?

P. Comments (add any other comments concerning the design and development of the curriculum):

III. Evaluation

A. Describe ways and the extent to which the design of the curriculum is consistent with the school's philosophy and objectives.

B. What procedures have been developed to carry on a continuous evaluation of the appropriateness of the curriculum design?

C. What are considered to be the special strengths of the curriculum? Cite evidence to support its effectiveness in these areas.

D. Identify those areas of the curriculum design that are in the greatest need of improvement. Cite evidence to support these needs.

E. If the school has been involved in major curriculum evaluation efforts during the past three years other than those noted above, please report them here and describe them briefly.

F. In what specific respects has the design of the curriculum been improved within the last three years? Why were these changes made?

IV. Plans for Improvement

A. Describe any curriculum changes planned or anticipated for the future.

B. Recommend, in order of priority, steps for the correction of weaknesses identified in the design of the curriculum.

C. Explain, citing specific reasons, why any of these desirable changes seem unattainable.

V. Current Status Scale

On the scale indicate with a check mark the present status of the school's curriculum design in relation to the school's stated philosophy and objectives.

Much
Improvement
Needed

Little or No
Improvement
Needed

Comments (add any other comments concerning the current status of the design of the school's curriculum):

Instructional Areas

NAME OF SCHOOL_____

DATE_____

Prepared by

_____   _____

_____   _____

_____   _____

NAME OF SUBJECT AREA _____

This section is designed to be used for all instructional areas. Each committee should react to the items as they apply to the respective instructional areas. If an item does not apply to a certain area, it should be so noted. Notes or qualifications that explain the responses or make more complete the description of the practices in the given area should be written in the proper spaces.

The committee given the responsibility for completing this section will find it beneficial to become thoroughly familiar with the entire section before attempting to react or respond to any part of it. It should be noted that this section is especially related to Section P, "Design of Curriculum."

The committee should recognize that Sections N and O titled "School and Community" and "Philosophy and Objectives" taken together form the foundation for the total evaluation. The responses in all other sections should reflect an awareness of the characteristics of both the school and the community and the influence of the statement of philosophy and objectives.

Although space has been provided throughout the section for committee responses, statements need not be limited to that space; the committee should feel free to attach addenda for items whose clarity will be improved by fuller development.

The report of this committee, when completed, should be presented to the entire faculty for approval or modification.

NATIONAL STUDY OF SCHOOL EVALUATION

5201 Leesburg Pike, Falls Church, Virginia 22041

Organization of the Criteria

The *Secondary School Evaluative Criteria: Narrative Edition* (Revised) is composed of fourteen sections as follows:

M	Manual
N1	School and Community (Public Schools)
N2	School and Community (Nonpublic Schools)
O	Phliosophy and Objectives
P	Design of Curriculum
Q	Instructional Areas
R	Individual Faculty Data
S	School Staff and Administration
T	Learning Media Services
U	Guidance Services
V	Auxiliary Services
W	Student Activities Program
X	School Plant and Facilities
Y	Plans and Priorities

The "Manual" provides an overview of the evaluation process and explains in some detail how the materials may be used. The section on "School and Community" together with the section on "Philosophy and Objectives" form the foundation for the process and undergird the entire evaluation.

"School and Community" is a data-gathering section. The section "School and Community (Nonpublic Schools)" is designed specifically for use by independent, church-related and other nonpublic schools. "Philosophy and Objectives" is designed to assist in developing or reexamining the school's existing philosophy and objectives in light of the data provided by the "School and Community" section.

The next two sections, "Design of Curriculum" and "Instructional Areas," are also closely related. "Design of Curriculum" focuses on the organization of the curriculum. It is extremely important that the subcommittee completing this section is a representative body of the total school program. The "Instructional Areas" section makes possible the evaluation of each of the areas of learning that the school identifies.

The section on "Individual Faculty Data" includes data concerning individual faculty members and provides opportunity for those persons to express opinions on certain aspects of the school program. This is the only section that each faculty member completes individually. The "School Staff and Administration" section gives attention to administration, instructional staff and auxiliary staff. The "Learning Media Services" section includes media services, library and audio-visual services. The "Guidance Services" section includes information about personal, educational and career counseling and the guidance program. The section entitled "Auxiliary Services" examines such services as those dealing with health, food and transportation. The "Student Activities Program" section focuses on the school's total activities program. The next section deals with the school plant and facilities. The final section, "Plans and Priorities," provides an opportunity to place in priority the school's plans for improvement.

The sections P, Q, S, T, U, V, W, and X use this common format:

    I. Principles
    II. Description
    III. Evaluation
    IV. Plans for Improvement
    V. Current Status Scale

This five-point format begins with Part I, a series of principles designed to stimulate thought and reflection about the school program. Part II consists of probing questions designed to elicit a description of the program or area under consideration. Part III provides an opportunity to appraise and evaluate the program described in the second part and Part IV asks for the school's plans for improvement. Part V gives the school an opportunity to indicate its status in comparison to an "optimum" program.

The School's Task in Evaluation

The complete evaluation of a school as recommended by the National Study of School Evaluation is a three-step process. The first step is a self-evaluation carried out by the faculty of the individual school. This step usually requires a minimum of one year. The second step is an evaluation by a visiting committee, which usually requires a minimum of three days. The third step is the school's consideration and follow-up of the findings of the evaluation.

The National Study of School Evaluation has developed a means for recognizing that schools which are quite different may be equally sound educationally. This concept involves the basic principle that a school shall be evaluated in terms of what it is striving to accomplish (its philosophy and objectives) and according to the extent to which it is meeting the needs of the students who are enrolled or for whom it is responsible. The philosophy and objectives of the school must be acceptable to some agency (a community, an accrediting association, a state department of education) if the evaluation is to be recognized beyond the confines of the school.

School staff and administration, parents, students and members of the governing body should be actively involved in this self-evaluation. It is important that all who are involved understand that the purpose of this self-study is to improve the quality of the school's program through the means of self-evaluation and comprehensive examination of what is happening to students in the school environment.

It is important to recognize that no one section of the self-study is meant to stand alone. Each section has been designed to correlate with other sections to form a comprehensive self-evaluation. It is important that participants not become single-minded when working on a particular section and overlook the fact that the total evaluation does not rest on that particular section. Staff interaction is essential in bringing about change.

This instrument is designed for a wide variety of secondary schools. Therefore, some items may not be applicable to a particular school situation. Schools are reminded of their prerogative to strike or change words, so long as they do not misdirect the intent of a statement but render it more relevant. In the event that an entire statement appears to be irrelevant, a school may decide it does not apply and explain its view in the space provided.

Finally, it is vital that each evaluation participant receives feedback on reports of all sections of the self-study and that each participant have an opportunity to express either agreement or disagreement with each report. Provision should be made for modification of a report when advisable.

More detailed information may be found in the "Manual," Section M.

I. Principles

Introduction

The instructional areas include all the courses of instruction that maintain and extend knowledge, attitudes, values and skills and that initiate new learning experiences.

Listed below are a number of specific principles regarding the areas of learning to which faculty, parents and students should address themselves. This introduction is designed to encourage introspection concerning this section of the self-study. It is a starting point for discussion and for interaction among participants preparatory to delving into the nature of this aspect of the school program. Participants should avoid lengthy debate over the adequacy or inadequacy of each principle. Rather, it is important that the committee assigned this responsibility react to each statement in terms of an overview of how the school community generally accepts and implements each principle.

The committee should indicate by circling the appropriate number in the first column to the right of each principle the extent to which that principle is accepted by the school and indicate by circling the appropriate number in the second column the extent to which that principle is being implemented in the school. Where necessary in order to be consistent with the stated philosophy and objectives specific principles may be modified and others added.

The descriptions of the numbers listed immediately below apply to the numbers in the columns to the right of the principles and should be borne in mind when marking the degree of acceptance and the degree of implementation.

Degree of Acceptance

1. Unacceptable
2. Questionable
3. Accept with reservations
4. Accept in general
5. Endorse completely

Degree of Implementation

1. Not implemented
2. Weakly implemented
3. Moderately implemented
4. Strongly implemented
5. Fully implemented

Principles

The content and learning activities in this instructional area:

	Degree Acceptance	Degree Implementation
1. Are based on the philosophy and objectives of the school	1 2 3 4 5	1 2 3 4 5
2. Are based on an assessment of student characteristics which affect the attainment of the objectives for this instructional area	1 2 3 4 5	1 2 3 4 5
3. Provide students with an opportunity to become increasingly responsible for their own learning program	1 2 3 4 5	1 2 3 4 5
4. Develop the basic skills and concepts which make up the core of this instructional area	1 2 3 4 5	1 2 3 4 5
5. Contribute to a balanced program of general education for each student	1 2 3 4 5	1 2 3 4 5
6. Provide for individual differences among students	1 2 3 4 5	1 2 3 4 5
7. Provide specific educational programs for all resident exceptional students	1 2 3 4 5	1 2 3 4 5
8. Allow specialists in the education of exceptional students to serve as consultants to other professsional staff members in the school	1 2 3 4 5	1 2 3 4 5
9. Are designed for exceptional students and complement the educational program of the school	1 2 3 4 5	1 2 3 4 5
10. Provide opportunities to discover and develop areas of interest and ability	1 2 3 4 5	1 2 3 4 5
11. Afford students an opportunity to identify, examine and learn to cope with current problems and issues in society	1 2 3 4 5	1 2 3 4 5
12. Are flexible enough to meet the changing needs of students.	1 2 3 4 5	1 2 3 4 5
13. Provide for evaluation of student achievement in accordance with each individual's aptitudes and abilities	1 2 3 4 5	1 2 3 4 5
14. Are analyzed continually to determine why some students do not succeed in some areas	1 2 3 4 5	1 2 3 4 5
15. Are systematically evaluated and updated on a regular basis	1 2 3 4 5	1 2 3 4 5
16. Are supported by teachers' participation in appropriate updating programs	1 2 3 4 5	1 2 3 4 5

17. Others

II. Description of the Program

Respond to each item and supply appropriate data.

A. List and describe briefly all course offerings in this instructional area and indicate those courses that are required and those that have prerequisites.

B. List the objectives for this instructional area.

C. Describe the methods that are utilized to determine how well these objectives are being achieved.

D. Indicate how well each of the objectives is being achieved. Attach summaries of such evidence.

E. Is the level of student achievement congruent with professional staff expectations? If not, identify areas of unsatisfactory achievement and list corrective measures being taken.

F. Describe the nature of the scope and sequence of instruction in this area, citing ways that balance and articulation are served.

G. In what ways are students provided an opportunity to assume responsibility in planning, carrying out and evaluating their own learning?

H. In what ways are opportunities provided for each student enrolled in this instructional area to identify and pursue interests and special talents?

I. In what ways are individual student's developmental needs and learning styles assessed and appropriate instructional activities provided?

J. In what ways are students aided in dealing with current issues and problems in our society which are appropriate to this instructional area?

K. What aspects of career education are attended to in this area of learning?

L. What provisions are made for students who have exceptional needs?

M. Do teachers use the results of evaluations as an index of their teaching effectiveness and do they make adjustments in teaching methods and materials accordingly? Give examples.

N. How do teachers work together in planning for the coordination of learning activities both within this instructional area and with other areas?

O. Describe the procedures used to inform the school's staff of available programs and services for exceptional students.

P. What inservice activities exist for staff members in this instructional area?

Q. Describe uses made of community resources (human and material) in this instructional area.

R. Discuss the adequacy or inadequacy of:

     1. Materials

2. Equipment

3. Facilities

S. Comments (add any other comments concerning this instructional area):

III. Evaluation

A. What improvements in the instructional program in this area have been completed within the past three years? Why were they made?

B. What are considered to be strengths of the content instruction in this area? Cite evidence, if available.

C. Identify those aspects of content and of instruction in this area that are in greatest need of strengthening. Cite evidence, if available.

IV. Plans and Recommendations for Improvement

Review the principles and data in this section and respond to the following:

A. List, in order of priority, the short-range improvements recommended for this learning area.

B. List, in order of priority, the long-range improvements recommended for this learning area.

C. Explain, citing specific reasons, why any of these desirable changes seem unattainable.

V. Current Status Scale

On the scale indicate with a check mark the present status of this area in relation to the school's stated philosophy and objectives and the community it serves.

Much
Improvement
Needed

Little or No
Improvement
Needed

Comments (add below any other comments concerning the current status of the educational program in this instructional area):

Individual Faculty Data

NAME_____

SCHOOL_____

DATE_____

    This section is to be completed by each member of the professional staff just before the completion of the self-study process. The data called for serve two purposes. First, to assist each staff member to make a considered examination of his present status as a professional person. Second, to provide a summary of information useful in viewing the staff of the school as a whole. Here, as in other sections, the staff member is encouraged to modify any item to make it more acceptable or understandable and also to feel free to provide any additional information that he feels will be helpful.

    Each staff member should keep a file of official documents related to his preparation and experiences.

NATIONAL STUDY OF SCHOOL EVALUATION
5201 Leesburg Pike, Falls Church, Virginia 22041

Organization of the Criteria

The *Secondary School Evaluative Criteria: Narrative Edition* (Revised) is composed of fourteen sections as follows:

M   Manual
N1   School and Community (Public Schools)
N2   School and Community (Nonpublic Schools)
O   Phliosophy and Objectives
P   Design of Curriculum
Q   Instructional Areas
R   Individual Faculty Data
S   School Staff and Administration
T   Learning Media Services
U   Guidance Services
V   Auxiliary Services
W   Student Activities Program
X   School Plant and Facilities
Y   Plans and Priorities

The "Manual" provides an overview of the evaluation process and explains in some detail how the materials may be used. The section on "School and Community" together with the section on "Philosophy and Objectives" form the foundation for the process and undergird the entire evaluation.

"School and Community" is a data-gathering section. The section "School and Community (Nonpublic Schools)" is designed specifically for use by independent, church-related and other nonpublic schools. "Philosophy and Objectives" is designed to assist in developing or reexamining the school's existing philosophy and objectives in light of the data provided by the "School and Community" section.

The next two sections, "Design of Curriculum" and "Instructional Areas," are also closely related. "Design of Curriculum" focuses on the organization of the curriculum. It is extremely important that the subcommittee compieting this section is a representative body of the total school program. The "Instructional Areas" section makes possible the evaluation of each of the areas of learning that the school identifies.

The section on "Individual Faculty Data" includes data concerning individual faculty members and provides opportunity for those persons to express opinions on certain aspects of the school program. This is the only section that each faculty member completes individually. The "School Staff and Administration" section gives attention to administration, instructional staff and auxiliary staff. The "Learning Media Services" section includes media services, library and audio-visual services. The "Guidance Services" section includes information about personal, educational and career counseling and the guidance program. The section entitled "Auxiliary Services" examines such services as those dealing with health, food and transportation. The "Student Activities Program" section focuses on the school's total activities program. The next section deals with the school plant and facilities. The final section, "Plans and Priorities," provides an opportunity to place in priority the school's plans for improvement.

The sections P, Q, S, T, U, V, W, and X use this common format:

   I. Principles
  II. Description
 III. Evaluation
 IV. Plans for Improvement
  V. Current Status Scale

This five-point format begins with Part I, a series of principles designed to stimulate thought and reflection about the school program. Part II consists of probing questions designed to elicit a description of the program or area under consideration. Part III provides an opportunity to appraise and evaluate the program described in the second part and Part IV asks for the school's plans for improvement. Part V gives the school an opportunity to indicate its status in comparison to an "optimum" program.

The School's Task in Evaluation

The complete evaluation of a school as recommended by the National Study of School Evaluation is a three-step process. The first step is a self-evaluation carried out by the faculty of the individual school. This step usually requires a minimum of one year. The second step is an evaluation by a visiting committee, which usually requires a minimum of three days. The third step is the school's consideration and follow-up of the findings of the evaluation.

The National Study of School Evaluation has developed a means for recognizing that schools which are quite different may be equally sound educationally. This concept involves the basic principle that a school shall be evaluated in terms of what it is striving to accomplish (its philosophy and objectives) and according to the extent to which it is meeting the needs of the students who are enrolled or for whom it is responsible. The philosophy and objectives of the school must be acceptable to some agency (a community, an accrediting association, a state department of education) if the evaluation is to be recognized beyond the confines of the school.

School staff and administration, parents, students and members of the governing body should be actively involved in this self-evaluation. It is important that all who are involved understand that the purpose of this self-study is to improve the quality of the school's program through the means of self-evaluation and comprehensive examination of what is happening to students in the school environment.

It is important to recognize that no one section of the self-study is meant to stand alone. Each section has been designed to correlate with other sections to form a comprehensive self-evaluation. It is important that participants not become single-minded when working on a particular section and overlook the fact that the total evaluation does not rest on that particular section. Staff interaction is essential in bringing about change.

This instrument is designed for a wide variety of secondary schools. Therefore, some items may not be applicable to a particular school situation. Schools are reminded of their prerogative to strike or change words, so long as they do not misdirect the intent of a statement but render it more relevant. In the event that an entire statement appears to be irrelevant, a school may decide it does not apply and explain its view in the space provided.

Finally, it is vital that each evaluation participant receives feedback on reports of all sections of the self-study and that each participant have an opportunity to express either agreement or disagreement with each report. Provision should be made for modification of a report when advisable.

More detailed information may be found in the "Manual," Section M.

PRINCIPLES

These principles are offered for your acceptance, rejection or modification. Please feel free to make changes.

A competent teaching staff is essential for a good school. The staff is a cooperating group of individually capable persons devoted to common educational purposes and motivated by a desire to develop the philosophy and work to attain the clearly formulated objectives of the school. Staff members should possess qualities of preparation, experience and attitude that contribute to effective learning. The number of staff members is adequate for the educational program, the school enrollment and the special needs of the students. The total working load is such that maximum efficiency in service is assured. Salaries are maintained at a level sufficient to ensure a standard of living comparable with social demands on the profession and to avoid the necessity for securing supplementary income.

Individual Faculty Data and Opinions

1. Name of faculty member _____

2. Teaching or other assignment _____

3. College and university preparation.

Institution	Years Attended	Degree	Major	Minor

4. Certificate(s) currently held (type and levels covered).

_____

_____

5. Summary of school experience.

Position and School	Dates of Service

6. Describe any significant nonschool experiences.

7. List professional affiliations, activities and experiences.

8. As an individual faculty member, what is your personal perception of this school, its role and its effectiveness? Describe factors which you believe either foster or inhibit school improvement.

9. What gains, if any, do you feel result from the self-study and evaluation process for the school? For you as an individual?

School Staff and Administration

NAME OF SCHOOL_____

DATE_____

Prepared by

_____   _____

_____   _____

This section comprises three subsections: Administration, Instructional Staff and Auxiliary Staff.

The committee given the responsibility for completing this section will find it beneficial to become thoroughly familiar with the entire section before attempting to react or respond to any part of it.

The committee should recognize that Sections N and O, titled "School and Community" and "Philosophy and Objectives," taken together form the foundation for the total evaluation. The responses in all other sections should reflect an awareness of the characteristics of both the school and the community and the influence of the statement of philosophy and objectives.

Although space has been provided throughout the section for committee responses, statements need not be limited to that space; the committee should feel free to attach addenda for items whose clarity will be improved by further development.

The report of this committee, when completed, should be presented to the entire faculty for approval or modification.

NATIONAL STUDY OF SCHOOL EVALUATION
5201 Leesburg Pike, Falls Church, Virginia 22041

Organization of the Criteria

The *Secondary School Evaluative Criteria: Narrative Edition* (Revised) is composed of fourteen sections as follows:

M   Manual
N1   School and Community (Public Schools)
N2   School and Community (Nonpublic Schools)
O   Phliosophy and Objectives
P   Design of Curriculum
Q   Instructional Areas
R   Individual Faculty Data
S   School Staff and Administration
T   Learning Media Services
U   Guidance Services
V   Auxiliary Services
W   Student Activities Program
X   School Plant and Facilities
Y   Plans and Priorities

The "Manual" provides an overview of the evaluation process and explains in some detail how the materials may be used. The section on "School and Community" together with the section on "Philosophy and Objectives" form the foundation for the process and undergird the entire evaluation.

"School and Community" is a data-gathering section. The section "School and Community (Nonpublic Schools)" is designed specifically for use by independent, church-related and other nonpublic schools. "Philosophy and Objectives" is designed to assist in developing or reexamining the school's existing philosophy and objectives in light of the data provided by the "School and Community" section.

The next two sections, "Design of Curriculum" and "Instructional Areas," are also closely related. "Design of Curriculum" focuses on the organization of the curriculum. It is extremely important that the subcommittee completing this section is a representative body of the total school program. The "Instructional Areas" section makes possible the evaluation of each of the areas of learning that the school identifies.

The section on "Individual Faculty Data" includes data concerning individual faculty members and provides opportunity for those persons to express opinions on certain aspects of the school program. This is the only section that each faculty member completes individually. The "School Staff and Administration" section gives attention to administration, instructional staff and auxiliary staff. The "Learning Media Services" section includes media services, library and audio-visual services. The "Guidance Services" section includes information about personal, educational and career counseling and the guidance program. The section entitled "Auxiliary Services" examines such services as those dealing with health, food and transportation. The "Student Activities Program" section focuses on the school's total activities program. The next section deals with the school plant and facilities. The final section, "Plans and Priorities," provides an opportunity to place in priority the school's plans for improvement.

The sections P, Q, S, T, U, V, W, and X use this common format:

I. Principles
II. Description
III. Evaluation
IV. Plans for Improvement
V. Current Status Scale

This five-point format begins with Part I, a series of principles designed to stimulate thought and reflection about the school program. Part II consists of probing questions designed to elicit a description of the program or area under consideration. Part III provides an opportunity to appraise and evaluate the program described in the second part and Part IV asks for the school's plans for improvement. Part V gives the school an opportunity to indicate its status in comparison to an "optimum" program.

The School's Task in Evaluation

The complete evaluation of a school as recommended by the National Study of School Evaluation is a three-step process. The first step is a self-evaluation carried out by the faculty of the individual school. This step usually requires a minimum of one year. The second step is an evaluation by a visiting committee, which usually requires a minimum of three days. The third step is the school's consideration and follow-up of the findings of the evaluation.

The National Study of School Evaluation has developed a means for recognizing that schools which are quite different may be equally sound educationally. This concept involves the basic principle that a school shall be evaluated in terms of what it is striving to accomplish (its philosophy and objectives) and according to the extent to which it is meeting the needs of the students who are enrolled or for whom it is responsible. The philosophy and objectives of the school must be acceptable to some agency (a community, an accrediting association, a state department of education) if the evaluation is to be recognized beyond the confines of the school.

School staff and administration, parents, students and members of the governing body should be actively involved in this self-evaluation. It is important that all who are involved understand that the purpose of this self-study is to improve the quality of the school's program through the means of self-evaluation and comprehensive examination of what is happening to students in the school environment.

It is important to recognize that no one section of the self-study is meant to stand alone. Each section has been designed to correlate with other sections to form a comprehensive self-evaluation. It is important that participants not become single-minded when working on a particular section and overlook the fact that the total evaluation does not rest on that particular section. Staff interaction is essential in bringing about change.

This instrument is designed for a wide variety of secondary schools. Therefore, some items may not be applicable to a particular school situation. Schools are reminded of their prerogative to strike or change words, so long as they do not misdirect the intent of a statement but render it more relevant. In the event that an entire statement appears to be irrelevant, a school may decide it does not apply and explain its view in the space provided.

Finally, it is vital that each evaluation participant receives feedback on reports of all sections of the self-study and that each participant have an opportunity to express either agreement or disagreement with each report. Provision should be made for modification of a report when advisable.

More detailed information may be found in the "Manual," Section M.

ADMINISTRATION

Throughout this section the following definitions shall apply.

Central office administration refers to any or all of the following: the superintendent, assistant superintendent(s), directors, supervisors, coordinators and similar district personnel.

Administrative staff of the school refers to any or all of the following: the principal, assistant principal(s), dean(s) and similar school personnel.

I. Principles

Introduction

The primary responsibility of the administration is to organize, supervise and manage the total school program in a manner consistent with the school's stated philosophy and objectives. Every condition of management and organization in a school is worthwhile to the extent that it is beneficial to teaching and learning and contributes to the society and community it serves. Correlating instruction, activities and services into an effective educational program requires talented and forward-looking leadership.

Listed below are a number of principles regarding administration that are generally held to be valid and to which the school community should address itself. This introduction is designed to encourage introspection concerning this section of the self-study. It is a starting point for discussion and for interaction among participants preparatory to delving into the nature of this aspect of the school program. Participants should avoid lengthy debate over the adequacy or the inadequacy of each principle. Rather, it is important that the committee assigned this responsibility react to each statement in terms of an overview of how the school community generally accepts and implements each principle.

Indicate by circling the appropriate number in the first column to the right of each principle the degree to which that principle is accepted by the school and indicate by circling the appropriate number in the second column the degree to which that principle is implemented in the school. Where necessary, in order to be consistent with your stated philosophy and objectives, principles may be modified and others added.

The descriptions of the numbers listed immediately below apply to the numbers in the columns to the right of the principle and should be borne in mind when marking the degree of acceptance and the degree of implementation.

Degree of Acceptance
1. Unacceptable
2. Questionable
3. Accept with reservations
4. Accept in general
5. Endorse completely

Degree of Implementation
1. Not implemented
2. Weakly implemented
3. Moderately implemented
4. Strongly implemented
5. Fully implemented

Principles

	Degree of Acceptance	Degree of Implementation
1. The administrative heads of the school district:		
Has full responsibility for the administration of the overall educational program and serves as administrator for, and executive officer of, the governing board	1 2 3 4 5	1 2 3 4 5
2. The governing board:		
Functions as the policy-making body for the school system	1 2 3 4 5	1 2 3 4 5
Has written comprehensive rules for determining its policies, organization and procedures	1 2 3 4 5	1 2 3 4 5
Clearly communicates to the administration, staff, students and community its policies and procedures	1 2 3 4 5	1 2 3 4 5
Provides leadership for the acquisition of facilities and equipment and for time, funds and leadership personnel necessary for implementing a desirable education program	1 2 3 4 5	1 2 3 4 5
Assists and encourages all administrators to participate in professional activities on local, state, regional and national levels	1 2 3 4 5	1 2 3 4 5
3. The central office administration regularly conducts research concerning educational problems and uses the results in planning educational programs	1 2 3 4 5	1 2 3 4 5
4. The school staff and school administration operate to implement the philosophy and objectives of the school	1 2 3 4 5	1 2 3 4 5
5. The administrative staff of the school through cooperative action with the central office staff is responsible for leadership that encourages, implements and evaluates effective instruction and reasonable experimentation	1 2 3 4 5	1 2 3 4 5

6. The principal:	Degree Acceptance	Degree Implementation
Provides leadership for the total school program	1 2 3 4 5	1 2 3 4 5
Provides leadership in the supervision and improvement of instruction based on the assessed needs of the students	1 2 3 4 5	1 2 3 4 5
Effectively utilizes staff members to provide an educational program	1 2 3 4 5	1 2 3 4 5
Appropriately delegates duties and authority in providing leadership in the school	1 2 3 4 5	1 2 3 4 5
Coordinates efforts to establish and maintain good community relations	1 2 3 4 5	1 2 3 4 5
Is well informed of educational developments	1 2 3 4 5	1 2 3 4 5
Provides for professional growth of the staff	1 2 3 4 5	1 2 3 4 5
Coordinates efforts to obtain maximum utilization of existing facilities, equipment, staff time and materials	1 2 3 4 5	1 2 3 4 5
Participates actively in the recruitment, selection, assignment and evaluation of school staff	1 2 3 4 5	1 2 3 4 5

7. Others

II. Description of the Program

A. School Staff

STAFF	NUMBER OF STAFF MEMBERS		Total Full Time Equivalent
	Full Time	Part Time	
1. Administrator(s)			
2. Supervisor(s)			
3. Classroom teachers			
4. Guidance counselor(s)			
5. Educational media personnel			
6. Health Service personnel			
7. Specialists and consultants			
8. Food services personnel			
9. Secretaries and clerks			
10. Custodial & maintenance personnel			
11. Paraprofessionals			
12. Transportation personnel			
13. Other			
Total			

B. List and describe briefly the responsibilities of regularly assigned members of the school staff who are assigned some administrative duties. Have job descriptions been written and are they available?

C. How is the administrative staff of the school organized and oriented to meet the administrative needs of the school as expressed in the philosophy and objectives? Is the administrative staff of the school sufficient in number to meet these needs? If the answer is no, describe needed services.

D. Describe the functional relationship among the principal of the school, the superintendent and the governing board.

E. Describe how the administrative staff of the school fulfills its responsibilities for:

   1. Staff supervision and evaluation.

   2. Professional growth.

   3. Leadership in program development.

4. Decision-making processes.

5. Community relations.

F. How does the administrative staff of the school encourage faculty members to seek ways of promoting human worth and dignity of the individual among the students?

G. In what ways does the administrative staff of the school:

1. Encourage faculty members to develop tolerance and understanding of the varied behavior of students?

2. Develop flexibility in attitudes toward change?

3. Accept behavior of colleagues which differs from their own?

H. How does the administrative staff of the school promote responsible student behavior?

I. How does the administrative staff of the school work with school-community organizations to improve the service the school renders to students?

J. Describe how the administrative staff of the school works with the central office staff in curriculum planning and development.

K. Describe what community involvement or participation takes place in developing school budgets?

L. Describe the professional participation of the administrative staff of the school in the following areas:

1. In inservice educational activities.

2. Attendance at workshops.

3. In professional organizations.

4. Additional study.

M. Comments (add any other comments concerning the school staff and administration of the school):

III. Evaluation

A. To what extent are the policies and procedures of the administrative staff of the school consistent with the philosophy and objectives of the school? Explain.

B. How effective are the operational procedures of the administrative staff of the school in meeting the needs of the school? Cite examples to support your response.

C. To what extent is the administrative staff of the school identifying and solving problems related to the total educational program?

D. Describe the procedures used to evaluate the administrative process on a regularly scheduled basis.

E. Identify those areas where the effectiveness of the administrative staff of the school needs strengthening.

F. Is the administrative staff of the school evaluated in light of the philosophy and objectives of the school? Explain.

IV. Plans for Improvement

A. List, in order of priority, the short-range plans for improving the effectiveness of the administrative staff of the school.

B. List, in order of priority, the long-range plans for improving the effectiveness of the administrative staff of the school.

C. Explain, citing specific reasons, why any of these desirable changes seem unattainable.

V. Current Status Scale

On the scale indicate with a check mark the present status of the administrative staff of the school in relation to the school's stated philosophy and objectives.

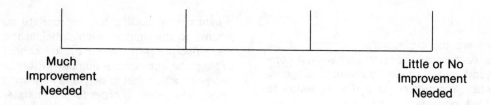

Much
Improvement
Needed

Little or No
Improvement
Needed

Comments (add any other comments concerning the current status of the school staff and administration):

INSTRUCTIONAL STAFF

I. Principles

Introduction

Instructional staff are the professional members of the school such as the teachers and department heads. A competent staff is essential to a sound educational program. The instructional staff, functioning as a unit, operates to implement the stated philosophy and objectives of the school program. Staff members have preparation, experience and attitudes that enable them to conduct activities that provide meaningful learning activities for students.

Listed below are a number of principles regarding the instructional staff which are generally held to be valid and to which the total school community should address itself. This introduction is designed to encourage introspection concerning this section of the self-study. It is a starting point for discussion and for interaction among participants preparatory to delving into the nature of this aspect of the school program. Participants should avoid lengthy debate over the adequacy or the inadequacy of each principle. Rather, it is important that the committee assigned this responsibility react to each statement in terms of an overview of how the school community generally accepts and implements each principle.

Indicate by circling the appropriate number in the first column to the right of each principle the degree to which that principle is accepted by the school and indicate by circling the appropriate number in the second column the degree to which that principle is implemented in the school. Where necessary, in order to be consistent with the stated philosophy and objectives, principles may be modified and others added.

The descriptions of the numbers listed immediately below apply to the numbered columns to the right of the principles and should be borne in mind when marking the degree of acceptance and the degree of implementation.

Degree of Acceptance

1. Unacceptable
2. Questionable
3. Accept with reservations
4. Accept in general
5. Endorse completely

Degree of Implementation

1. Not implemented
2. Weakly implemented
3. Moderately implemented
4. Strongly implemented
5. Fully implemented

Principles

	Degree Acceptance	Degree Implementation
1. The instructional staff cooperates to implement the philosophy and objectives of the school . . .	1 2 3 4 5	1 2 3 4 5
2. Each member of the instructional staff fosters a teaching-learning situation to meet the needs of the individual students . . .	1 2 3 4 5	1 2 3 4 5
3. Each member of the instructional staff evaluates his performance in terms of individual student growth . . .	1 2 3 4 5	1 2 3 4 5
4. The ratio of the instructional staff to pupils is adequate to provide meaningful learning experiences . . .	1 2 3 4 5	1 2 3 4 5
5. Members of the instructional staff maintain adequate preparation in their field of specialization . . .	1 2 3 4 5	1 2 3 4 5
6. Members of the instructional staff have a satisfactory knowledge of the nature and needs of adolescents and young adults . . .	1 2 3 4 5	1 2 3 4 5
7. The instructional staff is committed to providing for the individual learning needs of students . . .	1 2 3 4 5	1 2 3 4 5
8. The instructional staff works for self-improvement through appropriate activities . . .	1 2 3 4 5	1 2 3 4 5
9. Members of the instructional staff cooperate freely in curriculum development designed to improve the learning activities of students . . .	1 2 3 4 5	1 2 3 4 5
10. Members of the instructional staff show a willingness to develop and participate in innovative programs designed to improve instruction . . .	1 2 3 4 5	1 2 3 4 5

11. Others

II. Description of the Program

A. Experience distribution of instructional staff:

STAFF	YEARS OF EXPERIENCE			
	0–1	2–5	6–15	Over 15
Men				
Women				
Total				

B. Age distribution of instructional staff:

STAFF	AGE BRACKET										
	20–25	26–30	31–35	36–40	41–45	46–50	51–55	56–60	61–65	Over 65	Total
Men											
Women											
Total											

C. Academic preparation of professional staff:

STAFF	No Degree	B.S. or A.B.	A.B. Plus 40 Sem. Hrs. (no M.A.)	M.A.	Ed.S. or 6th yr.	Ph.D. Ed.D.
Men						
Women						
Total						

D. Professional preparation of faculty:

1. Number holding only an emergency certificate_____

2. Number holding a secondary school certificate_____

3. Other (specify)_____

_____

E. Respond to the following items and supply supporting evidence where it is requested or is valuable in explaining statements:

1. What is done to encourage the instructional staff to accomplish its responsibilities consistent with the stated philosophy and objectives?

2. What consideration is given to training, performance and competency in selecting a school staff?

3. In what ways are instructional staff members encouraged to improve professional competencies? Cite evidence that indicates the extent of recent professional growth.

4. Describe the nature and extent of the school staff's participation in the development of the school budget.

5. What awards and recognition are given to the instructional staff for the successful fulfillment of their duties and responsibilities?

6. Indicate the percent of change in the instructional staff for each of the last three years. Discuss the reasons for this change.

	number of staff	percent of change	Reasons
Current year			
One year ago			
Two years ago			

F. Comments (add any other comments concerning the nature of the instructional staff):

III. Evaluation

A. To what extent are the individual and collective goals of the instructional staff consistent with the philosophy and objectives of the school? Explain.

B. To what extent is the instructional staff involved in the identification of problems related to the instructional program of the school and seeking their solution? Explain.

C. Is the instructional staff evaluated on the basis of the school's philosophy? Explain.

D. What are the areas of special strength of the instructional staff?

E. Identify those areas in greatest need of strengthening in the instructional staff.

F. How would you rate the instructional staff morale? Give substantiating evidence.

IV. Plans for Improvement

A. List, in order of priority, the short-range plans for improving the effectiveness of the instructional staff.

B. List, in order of priority, the long-range plans for improving the effectiveness of the instructional staff of the school.

C. Explain, citing specific reasons, why any of these desirable changes seem unattainable.

V. Current Status Scale

On the scale indicate with a check mark the present status of the instructional staff of the school in relation to the school's stated philosophy and objectives.

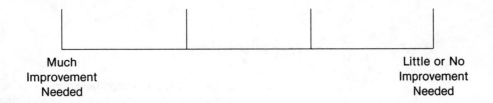

Much		Little or No
Improvement		Improvement
Needed		Needed

Comments (add any other comments concerning the current status of the instructional staff):

THE AUXILIARY STAFF

The auxiliary staff includes secretarial, clerical, cafeteria and similar workers.

I. Principles

Introduction

The members of the auxiliary staff make contributions to the total school program consistent with the philosophy and objectives of the school. Auxiliary staff members have experience, preparation and attitudes that are commensurate with their assignments.

Listed below are a number of principles regarding the auxiliary staff which are generally held to be valid and to which the total school community should address itself. This introduction is designed to encourage introspection concerning this section of the self-study. It is a starting point for discussion and for interaction among participants preparatory to delving into the nature of this aspect of the school program. Participants should avoid lengthy debate over the adequacy or the inadequacy of each principle. Rather, it is important that the committee assigned this responsibility react to each statement in terms of an overview of how the school community generally accepts and implements each principle.

Indicate by circling the appropriate number in the first column to the right of each principle the degree to which that principle is accepted by the school and indicate by circling the appropriate number in the second column the degree to which the principle is implemented in the school. Where necessary, in order to be consistent with your stated philosophy and objectives, principles may be modified and others added.

The descriptions of the numbers listed immediately below apply to the numbers in the columns to the right of the principles and should be borne in mind when marking the degree of acceptance and the degree of implementation.

Degree of Acceptance
1. Unacceptable
2. Questionable
3. Accept with reservations
4. Accept in general
5. Endorse completely

Degree of Implementation
1. Not implemented
2. Weakly implemented
3. Moderately implemented
4. Strongly implemented
5. Fully implemented

Principles

	Degree Acceptance	Degree Implementation
1. The principal is the administrative supervisor of the auxiliary staff	1 2 3 4 5	1 2 3 4 5
2. The role of each auxiliary staff member supports the educational program........	1 2 3 4 5	1 2 3 4 5
3. Recruiting, developing and retaining a well-qualified auxiliary staff is essential to the successful operation of the school	1 2 3 4 5	1 2 3 4 5
4. Career advancement is made available to auxiliary personnel through staff development opportunities...	1 2 3 4 5	1 2 3 4 5
5. Competent auxiliary personnel contribute to efficient school operation..........	1 2 3 4 5	1 2 3 4 5
6. Paraprofessionals are utilized to extend the services of the professional staff	1 2 3 4 5	1 2 3 4 5

7. Others

II. Description of the Program

Following are a number of items regarding the auxiliary staff. Respond to each and provide supporting data where requested.

A. List and describe briefly the responsibilities of reguarly assigned members of the auxiliary staff. Have job descriptions been written and are they available?

B. How is the auxiliary staff organized and assigned to meet the needs of the school as expressed in the philosophy and objectives of the school? Is the auxiliary staff sufficient in number to meet these needs? If not, describe the needed services.

C. Describe the school or school district's inservice training program for the auxiliary staff. Are auxiliary staff encouraged to participate?

D. Describe the school or school district's recruitment and selection program for auxiliary staff.

E. What methods are provided for evaluation and promotion of the auxiliary staff?

F. How does the school develop good communications among administrators, teachers, students and the auxiliary staff?

G. What provisions are made for retaining qualified and efficient members of the auxiliary staff?

H. Comments (add any other comments concerning the nature of the auxiliary staff):

III. Evaluation

A. How effective are the operational procedures of the auxiliary staff in meeting the needs of the school?

B. What improvements in the auxiliary services have been completed within the last three years?

C. What are the areas of special strength in the auxiliary services?

D. Identify those areas of the auxiliary services that are in greatest need of strengthening.

E. What procedures and practices are used in the regular evaluation of the auxiliary services?

IV. Plans for Improvement

A. List, in order of priority, the short-range plans for improving the effectiveness of the auxiliary staff of the school.

B. List, in order of priority, the long-range plans for improving the effectiveness of the auxiliary staff of the school.

V. Current Status Scale

On the scale indicate with a check mark the present status of the auxiliary staff of the school in relation to the school's stated philosophy and objectives.

Much
Improvement
Needed

Little or No
Improvement
Needed

Comments (add any other comments concerning the current status of the auxiliary staff):

Learning Media Services

NAME OF SCHOOL_____

DATE_____

Self-evaluation by

_____   _____

_____   _____

_____   _____

Indicate grade-level assignment of committee members where appropriate.

The committee given the responsibility of completing this section will find it beneficial to become thoroughly familiar with the entire section before attempting to react or respond to any part of it.

The committee should recognize that the "School and Community" and "Philosophy and Objectives" sections together form the foundation for the total evaluation. The responses in all other sections should reflect an awareness of the characteristics of both the school and community and the influence of the statements of philosophy and objectives.

Although space has been provided throughout the section for committee responses, statements need not be limited to that space; the committee should feel free to attach addenda for items where clarity will be improved by fuller development.

The completed report of this committee should be presented to the entire faculty for approval or modification.

NATIONAL STUDY OF SCHOOL EVALUATION
5201 Leesburg Pike, Falls Church, Virginia 22041

Organization of the Criteria

The *Secondary School Evaluative Criteria: Narrative Edition* (Revised) is composed of fourteen sections as follows:

M   Manual
N1   School and Community (Public Schools)
N2   School and Community (Nonpublic Schools)
O   Phliosophy and Objectives
P   Design of Curriculum
Q   Instructional Areas
R   Individual Faculty Data
S   School Staff and Administration
T   Learning Media Services
U   Guidance Services
V   Auxiliary Services
W   Student Activities Program
X   School Plant and Facilities
Y   Plans and Priorities

The "Manual" provides an overview of the evaluation process and explains in some detail how the materials may be used. The section on "School and Community" together with the section on "Philosophy and Objectives" form the foundation for the process and undergird the entire evaluation.

"School and Community" is a data-gathering section. The section "School and Community (Nonpublic Schools)" is designed specifically for use by independent, church-related and other nonpublic schools. "Philosophy and Objectives" is designed to assist in developing or reexamining the school's existing philosophy and objectives in light of the data provided by the "School and Community" section.

The next two sections, "Design of Curriculum" and "Instructional Areas," are also closely related. "Design of Curriculum" focuses on the organization of the curriculum. It is extremely important that the subcommittee completing this section is a representative body of the total school program. The "Instructional Areas" section makes possible the evaluation of each of the areas of learning that the school identifies.

The section on "Individual Faculty Data" includes data concerning individual faculty members and provides opportunity for those persons to express opinions on certain aspects of the school program. This is the only section that each faculty member completes individually. The "School Staff and Administration" section gives attention to administration, instructional staff and auxiliary staff. The "Learning Media Services" section includes media services, library and audio-visual services. The "Guidance Services" section includes information about personal, educational and career counseling and the guidance program. The section entitled "Auxiliary Services" examines such services as those dealing with health, food and transportation. The "Student Activities Program" section focuses on the school's total activities program. The next section deals with the school plant and facilities. The final section, "Plans and Priorities," provides an opportunity to place in priority the school's plans for improvement.

The sections P, Q, S, T, U, V, W, and X use this common format:

  I. Principles
 II. Description
III. Evaluation
IV. Plans for Improvement
 V. Current Status Scale

This five-point format begins with Part I, a series of principles designed to stimulate thought and reflection about the school program. Part II consists of probing questions designed to elicit a description of the program or area under consideration. Part III provides an opportunity to appraise and evaluate the program described in the second part and Part IV asks for the school's plans for improvement. Part V gives the school an opportunity to indicate its status in comparison to an "optimum" program.

The School's Task in Evaluation

The complete evaluation of a school as recommended by the National Study of School Evaluation is a three-step process. The first step is a self-evaluation carried out by the faculty of the individual school. This step usually requires a minimum of one year. The second step is an evaluation by a visiting committee, which usually requires a minimum of three days. The third step is the school's consideration and follow-up of the findings of the evaluation.

The National Study of School Evaluation has developed a means for recognizing that schools which are quite different may be equally sound educationally. This concept involves the basic principle that a school shall be evaluated in terms of what it is striving to accomplish (its philosophy and objectives) and according to the extent to which it is meeting the needs of the students who are enrolled or for whom it is responsible. The philosophy and objectives of the school must be acceptable to some agency (a community, an accrediting association, a state department of education) if the evaluation is to be recognized beyond the confines of the school.

School staff and administration, parents, students and members of the governing body should be actively involved in this self-evaluation. It is important that all who are involved understand that the purpose of this self-study is to improve the quality of the school's program through the means of self-evaluation and comprehensive examination of what is happening to students in the school environment.

It is important to recognize that no one section of the self-study is meant to stand alone. Each section has been designed to correlate with other sections to form a comprehensive self-evaluation. It is important that participants not become single-minded when working on a particular section and overlook the fact that the total evaluation does not rest on that particular section. Staff interaction is essential in bringing about change.

This instrument is designed for a wide variety of secondary schools. Therefore, some items may not be applicable to a particular school situation. Schools are reminded of their prerogative to strike or change words, so long as they do not misdirect the intent of a statement but render it more relevant. In the event that an entire statement appears to be irrelevant, a school may decide it does not apply and explain its view in the space provided.

Finally, it is vital that each evaluation participant receives feedback on reports of all sections of the self-study and that each participant have an opportunity to express either agreement or disagreement with each report. Provision should be made for modification of a report when advisable.

More detailed information may be found in the "Manual," Section M.

I. Principles

Introduction

The teacher uses resources in and out of the classroom to guide individual students in learning. Educational and technological advancements help teachers as they attempt to make learning more meaningful to the student.

The development of a variety of new materials and the merging of the audio-visual center with the library have provided teachers and students with a wealth of resources, generally found in a single location. To describe this learning environment, the term "learning media center" has been created and the term "learning media services" is used to describe the functions of such a center.

Three categories of facilities are recognized today as essential to fulfill the functions of the media center:

1. Learning facilities—in which the students, individually or as a group, are brought together with media for the purpose of learning.
2. Facilities for storage and access—in which media in various forms are cataloged, stored and made accessible for learning situations.
3. Production and supporting facilities—in which media in a variety of forms are produced to meet particular learning requirements and where teaching staff and students receive assistance and support in the effective and efficient use of media.

Listed below are a number of specific principles regarding the "Learning Media Services" to which faculty, parents and students should address themselves. This introductory part is designed to encourage introspection of the concerns covered by this section of the self-study. It is a starting point for discussion and for interaction among participants before they delve into the nature of this aspect of the school program. Participants should avoid lengthy debate over the adequacy or the inadequacy of each principle. Rather, it is important that the committee assigned this responsibility react to each statement in terms of an overview of how the school community generally accepts and implements each principle.

The committee should indicate by circling the appropriate number in the first column to the right of each principle the extent to which that principle is accepted by the school and indicate by circling the appropriate number in the second column the extent to which that principle is being implemented in the school. Where necessary, in order to be consistent with the stated philosophy and objectives, specific principles may be modified and others added.

The descriptions of the numbers listed below apply to the numbers in the columns to the right of the principles and should be borne in mind when marking the degree of acceptance and the degree of implementation.

Degree of Acceptance	Degree of Implementation
1. Unacceptable	1. Not implemented
2. Questionable	2. Weakly implemented
3. Accept with reservations	3. Moderately implemented
4. Accept in general	4. Strongly implemented
5. Endorse completely	5. Fully implemented

Principles

	Degree Acceptance	Degree Implementation
1. The learning media center is centrally located, easily accessible and open at such times to encourage optimum use of the materials and equipment	1 2 3 4 5	1 2 3 4 5
2. The quantity of the media center equipment is directly related to the objectives of the educational program	1 2 3 4 5	1 2 3 4 5
3. The quality of the media center equipment is directly related to the objectives of the educational program	1 2 3 4 5	1 2 3 4 5
4. The quantity of the media center materials is directly related to the objectives of the educational program	1 2 3 4 5	1 2 3 4 5
5. The quality of the media center materials is directly related to the objectives of the educational program	1 2 3 4 5	1 2 3 4 5
6. The learning media center is arranged in such a way that diverse activities can be carried on simultaneously	1 2 3 4 5	1 2 3 4 5
7. As teaching aids and equipment are developed, members of the teaching staff, along with the center staff, evaluate them as potential additions to the learning media center	1 2 3 4 5	1 2 3 4 5
8. Materials and equipment for the learning media center are selected on the basis of their contribution to the overall school program	1 2 3 4 5	1 2 3 4 5
9. Teachers and students are given orientation on the use of materials and equipment in the learning media center	1 2 3 4 5	1 2 3 4 5
10. Students are given orientation on the use of materials and equipment in the learning media center	1 2 3 4 5	1 2 3 4 5

	Degree Acceptance	Degree Implementation

11. Financial provision is made for the maintenance and continuous development of the learning media center and services .... 1 2 3 4 5 | 1 2 3 4 5

12. The learning media staff, both professional and nonprofessional, is adequate to provide effective service to the students and faculty .... 1 2 3 4 5 | 1 2 3 4 5

13. The learning media staff includes persons (probably noncertificated) who are skilled in the preparation, maintenance and repair of materials and equipment .. 1 2 3 4 5 | 1 2 3 4 5

14. The professional members of the learning media staff have specialized preparation in the organization and administration of library and audio-visual services .. 1 2 3 4 5 | 1 2 3 4 5

15. The professional members of the learning media staff are an integral part of the regular faculty.. 1 2 3 4 5 | 1 2 3 4 5

16. Students are actively involved in the operation of the media center .... 1 2 3 4 5 | 1 2 3 4 5

17. The learning media staff facilitates individualized and group learning .... 1 2 3 4 5 | 1 2 3 4 5

18. The teaching staff is responsible for stimulating the effective utilization of media resources by students .... 1 2 3 4 5 | 1 2 3 4 5

19. Other

II. Description of the Learning Media Services

A. In the table below fill in those blanks that are applicable to the learning media staff of your school.

STAFF	FULL TIME Number	PART TIME Number	Total Hours per Week
Professional			
Paraprofessional			
Students	✕		
Volunteers			

B. Who is responsible for coordination of the learning media services? Describe positions, duties and responsibilities.

C. Indicate the distribution of responsibilities for learning media services among other professional and paraprofessional members of the learning media staff.

D. Do all members of the learning media staff (both professional and paraprofessional) have special training in their areas of responsibility? Specify the extent and recency of the special training.

E. Analyze the following aspects of the learning media center.

   1. Space (such as areas for reading, viewing, listening, instruction, individual study, shelving, storage of materials, processing and production of materials and offices for personnel).

      Adequacies:

Inadequacies (if any):

2. Equipment (e.g., projectors—motion picture, overhead, opaque, slide and filmstrip—screens, tape recorders, TV sets, video equipment, computers, record players, radios, copy machines, study carrels and materials production tools).

   Adequacies:

   Inadequacies (if any):

3. Materials (e.g., books, magazines, newspapers, films, filmstrips, film loops, computer software, slides, tapes, records, transparencies, pictures, charts, maps, globes, paperbacks, community resource file, programmed instruction materials and special materials for the professional library).

    Adequacies:

    Inadequacies (if any):

4. Special materials for students with unique needs (e.g., large print editions, taped textbooks, Braille editions, multi-ethnic and bilingual materials).

    Adequacies:

Inadequacies (if any):

5. Budget (adequate to fulfill needs of students and staff, provide normal replacement and improvement and provide for innovation). Indicate overall budget each year for the past three years.

Adequacies:

Inadequacies (if any):

F. What circulation records are kept to indicate the use of the equipment and materials in the learning media center?

G. Do the records show patterns or trends in the frequency of use of facilities, equipment and materials? If so, indicate their significance for future planning.

H. Is the learning media center open to students and teachers at other than regular school hours? Explain.

I. Discuss the procedure involved in the selection of new equipment and materials.

J. What procedures are followed to respond to concerns regarding the appropriateness of materials in the collection? Attach a copy of the policy outlining these procedures.

K. Discuss the procedure for keeping equipment and materials current, i.e., the discarding of outdated or unused items.

L. What provisions are made for the systematic orientation of new students on the use and the educational potential of the learning media center and services?

M. What provisions are made for the systematic orientation of new teachers on the use and educational potential of the learning media center and services?

N. What provisions are made to use resources available from the community, larger service units and commercial agencies to supplement the services of the learning media center?

O. Comments (add any other comments concerning the school's learning media center):

III. Evaluation

A. What improvements in the learning media services have been completed within the past three years?

B. In what ways are available learning media services consistent with the school's stated philosophy and objectives?

C. What are the areas of special strength in the learning media services?

D. Identify those areas of the learning media services that are in greatest need of strengthening.

E. What procedures and practices are used in the continuous evaluation of the learning media services?

IV. Plans for Improvement

A. List, in order of priority, the short-range improvements planned for the learning media services.

B. List, in order of priority, the long-range improvements that are planned for the learning media services.

C. Explain, citing specific reasons, why any of these desirable changes seem unattainable.

V. Current Status Scale

On the scale indicate with a check mark the present status of the learning media services in relation to the school's stated philosophy and objectives.

Much
Improvement
Needed

Little or No
Improvement
Needed

Comments (add any other comments concerning the current status of the school's learning media services):

Guidance Services

NAME OF SCHOOL _____

DATE _____

Prepared by

_____   _____

_____   _____

_____   _____

Student guidance services include personal educational and career counseling that the school makes available to students. These services contribute to solutions to the academic, personal, social, physical and occupational problems of students.

The committee given responsibility for completing this section will find it beneficial to become thoroughly familiar with the entire section before attempting to react or respond to any part of it.

The committee should recognize that Sections N and O, titled "School and Community" and "Philosophy and Objectives," taken together form the foundation for the total evaluation.

The responses in all other sections should reflect an awareness of the characteristics of both the school and the community and the influence of the statements of philosophy and objectives.

Although space has been provided throughout the section for committee responses, statements need not be limited to that space; the committee should feel free to attach addenda for items whose clarity will be improved by fuller development.

The report of this committee, when completed, should be presented to the entire faculty for approval or modification.

NATIONAL STUDY OF SCHOOL EVALUATION
5201 Leesburg Pike, Falls Church, Virginia 22041

Organization of the Criteria

The *Secondary School Evaluative Criteria: Narrative Edition* (Revised) is composed of fourteen sections as follows:

M	Manual
N1	School and Community (Public Schools)
N2	School and Community (Nonpublic Schools)
O	Phliosophy and Objectives
P	Design of Curriculum
Q	Instructional Areas
R	Individual Faculty Data
S	School Staff and Administration
T	Learning Media Services
U	Guidance Services
V	Auxiliary Services
W	Student Activities Program
X	School Plant and Facilities
Y	Plans and Priorities

The "Manual" provides an overview of the evaluation process and explains in some detail how the materials may be used. The section on "School and Community" together with the section on "Philosophy and Objectives" form the foundation for the process and undergird the entire evaluation.

"School and Community" is a data-gathering section. The section "School and Community (Nonpublic Schools)" is designed specifically for use by independent, church-related and other nonpublic schools. "Philosophy and Objectives" is designed to assist in developing or reexamining the school's existing philosophy and objectives in light of the data provided by the "School and Community" section.

The next two sections, "Design of Curriculum" and "Instructional Areas," are also closely related. "Design of Curriculum" focuses on the organization of the curriculum. It is extremely important that the subcommittee completing this section is a representative body of the total school program. The "Instructional Areas" section makes possible the evaluation of each of the areas of learning that the school identifies.

The section on "Individual Faculty Data" includes data concerning individual faculty members and provides opportunity for those persons to express opinions on certain aspects of the school program. This is the only section that each faculty member completes individually. The "School Staff and Administration" section gives attention to administration, instructional staff and auxiliary staff. The "Learning Media Services" section includes media services, library and audio-visual services. The "Guidance Services" section includes information about personal, educational and career counseling and the guidance program. The section entitled "Auxiliary Services" examines such services as those dealing with health, food and transportation. The "Student Activities Program" section focuses on the school's total activities program. The next section deals with the school plant and facilities. The final section, "Plans and Priorities," provides an opportunity to place in priority the school's plans for improvement.

The sections P, Q, S, T, U, V, W, and X use this common format:

    I. Principles
    II. Description
    III. Evaluation
    IV. Plans for Improvement
    V. Current Status Scale

This five-point format begins with Part I, a series of principles designed to stimulate thought and reflection about the school program. Part II consists of probing questions designed to elicit a description of the program or area under consideration. Part III provides an opportunity to appraise and evaluate the program described in the second part and Part IV asks for the school's plans for improvement. Part V gives the school an opportunity to indicate its status in comparison to an "optimum" program.

The School's Task in Evaluation

The complete evaluation of a school as recommended by the National Study of School Evaluation is a three-step process. The first step is a self-evaluation carried out by the faculty of the individual school. This step usually requires a minimum of one year. The second step is an evaluation by a visiting committee, which usually requires a minimum of three days. The third step is the school's consideration and follow-up of the findings of the evaluation.

The National Study of School Evaluation has developed a means for recognizing that schools which are quite different may be equally sound educationally. This concept involves the basic principle that a school shall be evaluated in terms of what it is striving to accomplish (its philosophy and objectives) and according to the extent to which it is meeting the needs of the students who are enrolled or for whom it is responsible. The philosophy and objectives of the school must be acceptable to some agency (a community, an accrediting association, a state department of education) if the evaluation is to be recognized beyond the confines of the school.

School staff and administration, parents, students and members of the governing body should be actively involved in this self-evaluation. It is important that all who are involved understand that the purpose of this self-study is to improve the quality of the school's program through the means of self-evaluation and comprehensive examination of what is happening to students in the school environment.

It is important to recognize that no one section of the self-study is meant to stand alone. Each section has been designed to correlate with other sections to form a comprehensive self-evaluation. It is important that participants not become single-minded when working on a particular section and overlook the fact that the total evaluation does not rest on that particular section. Staff interaction is essential in bringing about change.

This instrument is designed for a wide variety of secondary schools. Therefore, some items may not be applicable to a particular school situation. Schools are reminded of their prerogative to strike or change words, so long as they do not misdirect the intent of a statement but render it more relevant. In the event that an entire statement appears to be irrelevant, a school may decide it does not apply and explain its view in the space provided.

Finally, it is vital that each evaluation participant receives feedback on reports of all sections of the self-study and that each participant have an opportunity to express either agreement or disagreement with each report. Provision should be made for modification of a report when advisable.

More detailed information may be found in the "Manual," Section M.

GUIDANCE SERVICES

I. Principles

Introduction

The complexity, multiplicity and depth of the personal, social, emotional and physical problems that high school students face make it necessary for adults to work closely with them. School leadership in this important phase of the student's education should come from the student personnel staff.

Listed below are a number of principles regarding student services that are generally held to be valid and to which the school community should address itself. This introduction is designed to encourage introspection concerning this section of the self-study. It is a starting point for discussion and for interaction among participants preparatory to delving into the nature of this aspect of the school program. Participants should avoid lengthy debate over the adequacy or the inadequacy of each principle. Rather, it is important that the committee assigned this responsibility react to each statement in terms of an overview of how the school community generally accepts and implements each principle.

Indicate by circling the appropriate number in the first column to the right of each principle the degree to which that principle is accepted by the school and indicate by circling the appropriate number in the second column the degree to which that principle is implemented in the school. Where necessary, in order to be consistent with the school's stated philosophy and objectives, principles may be modified or others added.

The descriptions of the numbers listed below apply to the numbers in the columns to the right of the principles and should be borne in mind when marking the degree of acceptance and the degree of implementation.

Degree of Acceptance	Degree of Implementation
1. Unacceptable	1. Not implemented
2. Questionable	2. Weakly implemented
3. Accept with reservations	3. Moderately implemented
4. Accept in general	4. Strongly implemented
5. Endorse completely	5. Fully implemented

Principles — Guidance Services

	Degree Acceptance	Degree Implementation
1. Guidance services encompass specified activities that provide a means whereby counselors, parents, teachers and school administrators may assist the students in developing individual plans to realize their full potential	1 2 3 4 5	1 2 3 4 5
2. The relationships between guidance personnel and instructional and administrative staff are clear	1 2 3 4 5	1 2 3 4 5
3. The guidance staff has a sufficient diversity of background, training and interests to serve the varied needs of all students	1 2 3 4 5	1 2 3 4 5
4. Guidance personnel make maximum use of their time and effort in order to provide needed services to students	1 2 3 4 5	1 2 3 4 5
5. Guidance personnel aid the teachers in helping students with learning problems	1 2 3 4 5	1 2 3 4 5
6. Student personnel records are adequate and accurate	1 2 3 4 5	1 2 3 4 5
7. Security measures are taken to protect the integrity of the individual student's record for authorized and professional use	1 2 3 4 5	1 2 3 4 5
8. Adequate provision is made for the interpretation of essential information to instructional staff, pupils, parents and administrators	1 2 3 4 5	1 2 3 4 5
9. Provision is made for effective use of the services of counselors, school nurses, social workers, specialists on the education of exceptional students and other professional personnel	1 2 3 4 5	1 2 3 4 5
10. Identification of the needs of exceptional students is accomplished through referral to the guidance department by teachers, administrators, parents and physicians and through established screening programs in the school and community	1 2 3 4 5	1 2 3 4 5
11. Placement in a special class or program is a decision arrived at by a team of professionals meeting with the parents to determine the best educational plans for the student	1 2 3 4 5	1 2 3 4 5

	Degree Acceptance					Degree Implementation				
12. All programs for exceptional students contribute to the obtaining of the high school diploma	1	2	3	4	5	1	2	3	4	5
13. There is extensive articulation among the various levels in the system to ensure continuity of curriculum and records	1	2	3	4	5	1	2	3	4	5
14. The guidance department conducts follow-up studies of high school graduates	1	2	3	4	5	1	2	3	4	5
15. The guidance department provides occupational information and placement services	1	2	3	4	5	1	2	3	4	5

16. Others

II. Description of the Program

A. What are the major objectives of the guidance program?

B. How are the guidance services organized and administered?

C. What preparation, experience and personal qualifications are represented by the guidance staff?

D. Describe the major task of a counselor and indicate the time allotted for each task.

E. Indicate the number of students assigned to each counselor and the basis of assignment.

F. Describe the guidance facilities and discuss their adequacy.

G. What resources and specialists within the school and community are available for use in guidance service activities?

H. Is there an adviser–advisee program? If so, explain.

I. Are paraprofessional personnel used in the advisement program? If so, explain.

J. How is specialized counseling and testing coordinated between community agencies and the school staff?

K. Explain how student information from previous schools is used.

L. What provisions are made for interpretation of the test results to pupils, parents, instructional staff and administrators?

M. Explain how extensively information from student records is used by (be explicit):

   1. Guidance personnel

   2. Instructional staff

3. School administrators

4. Others (list):

N. How are the student records of the guidance services prepared, organized, filed and secured? Are there specific guidelines for these activities?

O. How are students grouped for instruction and what are the specific criteria for such grouping?

P. In what ways are guidance personnel involved with administrative and instructional staff in developing worthwhile programs for individual students?

Q. Describe the ways guidance services are provided for exceptional students?

R. How are exceptional students identified?

S. Describe the program for communicating with and involving parents of exceptional students.

T. What steps are taken to provide educational counseling and guidance services for *all* students in the school?

U. What group counseling and guidance procedures are used?

V. What professional growth programs are available to keep teaching staff and all guidance personnel abreast of new techniques and developments in guidance services?

W. In providing guidance services to students in this school are there specific problems that tend to reappear consistently? If so, indicate the nature of the problem(s), corrective measures tried and the effectiveness of the corrective measures.

X. Describe the nature and extent of any work experience program.

Y. What steps are taken to provide direction and counseling to all students in making personal, career and occupational choices?

Z. Describe procedures in the identification of available job opportunities and the process employed to utilize job opportunities.

AA. What information is gathered about students who leave school prior to graduation (i.e., transfers, drop-outs, etc.)?

BB. Describe the program of follow-up studies of school graduates. What uses are made of these data?

CC. Comments (add any other comments concerning the guidance services):

III. Evaluation

A. Cite evidence that the guidance services are consistent with the school's stated philosophy and objectives.

B. What improvements in the guidance services have been completed within the past three years?

C. What are the areas of special strength in the guidance services?

D. Identify those areas of the guidance services that are in greatest need of strengthening.

E. What procedures and practices are used in the continuous evaluation of the services?

IV. Plans for Improvement

A. List, in order of priority, the short-range improvements for the guidance services.

B. List, in order of priority, the long-range improvements for the guidance services.

C. Explain, citing specific reasons, why any of these desirable changes seem unattainable.

V. Current Status Scale

On the scale please indicate with a check mark the present status of the guidance services in relation to the school's stated philosophy and objectives.

Much Improvement Needed	Little or No Improvement Needed

Comments (add any other comments concerning the current status of the school's learning media services):

Auxiliary Services

NAME OF SCHOOL _____

DATE _____

Prepared by

_____   _____

_____   _____

_____

Student auxiliary services include all those services which the school makes available to students that are non-instructional and nonadministrative in nature.

In this section, special emphasis is given to health services, food services and transportation services. The committee given responsibility for evaluating this section will find it beneficial to include representatives from each of the areas mentioned. It is further suggested that the committee become thoroughly familiar with the entire section before attempting to react or respond to any part of it.

The committee should recognize that Sections N and O, titled "School and Community" and "Philosophy and Objec-tives," taken together form the foundation for the total evaluation. The responses in all other sections should reflect an awareness of the characteristics of both the school and the community and the influence of the statements of philosophy and objectives.

Although space has been provided throughout the section for committee responses, statements need not be limited to that space; the committee should feel free to attach addenda for items whose clarity will be improved by fuller development.

The report of this committee, when completed, should be presented to the entire faculty for approval or modification.

NATIONAL STUDY OF SCHOOL EVALUATION
5201 Leesburg Pike, Falls Church, Virginia 22041

Organization of the Criteria

The *Secondary School Evaluative Criteria: Narrative Edition* (Revised) is composed of fourteen sections as follows:

M   Manual
N1   School and Community (Public Schools)
N2   School and Community (Nonpublic Schools)
O   Phliosophy and Objectives
P   Design of Curriculum
Q   Instructional Areas
R   Individual Faculty Data
S   School Staff and Administration
T   Learning Media Services
U   Guidance Services
V   Auxiliary Services
W   Student Activities Program
X   School Plant and Facilities
Y   Plans and Priorities

The "Manual" provides an overview of the evaluation process and explains in some detail how the materials may be used. The section on "School and Community" together with the section on "Philosophy and Objectives" form the foundation for the process and undergird the entire evaluation.

"School and Community" is a data-gathering section. The section "School and Community (Nonpublic Schools)" is designed specifically for use by independent, church-related and other nonpublic schools. "Philosophy and Objectives" is designed to assist in developing or reexamining the school's existing philosophy and objectives in light of the data provided by the "School and Community" section.

The next two sections, "Design of Curriculum" and "Instructional Areas," are also closely related. "Design of Curriculum" focuses on the organization of the curriculum. It is extremely important that the subcommittee completing this section is a representative body of the total school program. The "Instructional Areas" section makes possible the evaluation of each of the areas of learning that the school identifies.

The section on "Individual Faculty Data" includes data concerning individual faculty members and provides opportunity for those persons to express opinions on certain aspects of the school program. This is the only section that each faculty member completes individually. The "School Staff and Administration" section gives attention to administration, instructional staff and auxiliary staff. The "Learning Media Services" section includes media services, library and audio-visual services. The "Guidance Services" section includes information about personal, educational and career counseling and the guidance program. The section entitled "Auxiliary Services" examines such services as those dealing with health, food and transportation. The "Student Activities Program" section focuses on the school's total activities program. The next section deals with the school plant and facilities. The final section, "Plans and Priorities," provides an opportunity to place in priority the school's plans for improvement.

The sections P, Q, S, T, U, V, W, and X use this common format:

    I. Principles
   II. Description
  III. Evaluation
  IV. Plans for Improvement
   V. Current Status Scale

This five-point format begins with Part I, a series of principles designed to stimulate thought and reflection about the school program. Part II consists of probing questions designed to elicit a description of the program or area under consideration. Part III provides an opportunity to appraise and evaluate the program described in the second part and Part IV asks for the school's plans for improvement. Part V gives the school an opportunity to indicate its status in comparison to an "optimum" program.

The School's Task in Evaluation

The complete evaluation of a school as recommended by the National Study of School Evaluation is a three-step process. The first step is a self-evaluation carried out by the faculty of the individual school. This step usually requires a minimum of one year. The second step is an evaluation by a visiting committee, which usually requires a minimum of three days. The third step is the school's consideration and follow-up of the findings of the evaluation.

The National Study of School Evaluation has developed a means for recognizing that schools which are quite different may be equally sound educationally. This concept involves the basic principle that a school shall be evaluated in terms of what it is striving to accomplish (its philosophy and objectives) and according to the extent to which it is meeting the needs of the students who are enrolled or for whom it is responsible. The philosophy and objectives of the school must be acceptable to some agency (a community, an accrediting association, a state department of education) if the evaluation is to be recognized beyond the confines of the school.

School staff and administration, parents, students and members of the governing body should be actively involved in this self-evaluation. It is important that all who are involved understand that the purpose of this self-study is to improve the quality of the school's program through the means of self-evaluation and comprehensive examination of what is happening to students in the school environment.

It is important to recognize that no one section of the self-study is meant to stand alone. Each section has been designed to correlate with other sections to form a comprehensive self-evaluation. It is important that participants not become single-minded when working on a particular section and overlook the fact that the total evaluation does not rest on that particular section. Staff interaction is essential in bringing about change.

This instrument is designed for a wide variety of secondary schools. Therefore, some items may not be applicable to a particular school situation. Schools are reminded of their prerogative to strike or change words, so long as they do not misdirect the intent of a statement but render it more relevant. In the event that an entire statement appears to be irrelevant, a school may decide it does not apply and explain its view in the space provided.

Finally, it is vital that each evaluation participant receives feedback on reports of all sections of the self-study and that each participant have an opportunity to express either agreement or disagreement with each report. Provision should be made for modification of a report when advisable.

More detailed information may be found in the "Manual," Section M.

HEALTH SERVICES

I. Principles

Introduction

School health services include a variety of activities designed to assist in protecting or improving student health. They also secure the information needed to assist the school in adapting programs to the mental and physical needs and abilities of early adolescents. The program of school health services should be concerned with all aspects of health—physical, mental, emotional and social. It should be closely related to the guidance services.

Listed below are a number of principles regarding school health services that are generally held to be valid and to which the school community should address itself. This introduction is designed to encourage introspection concerning this section of the self-study. It is a starting point for discussion and for interaction among participants preparatory to delving into the nature of this aspect of the school program. Participants should avoid lengthy debate over the adequacy or the inadequacy of each principle. Rather, it is important that the committee assigned this responsibility react to each statement in terms of an overview of how the school community generally accepts and implements each principle.

Indicate by circling the appropriate number in the first column to the right of each principle the degree to which that principle is accepted by the school and indicate by circling the appropriate number in the second column the degree to which that principle is implemented in the school. Where necessary, in order to be consistent with the school's stated philosophy and objectives, principles may be modified or others added.

The description of the numbers listed below apply to the numbers in the columns to the right of the principle and should be borne in mind when marking the degree of acceptance and the degree of implementation.

Degree of Acceptance	Degree of Implementation
1. Unacceptable	1. Not implemented
2. Questionable	2. Weakly implemented
3. Accept with reservations	3. Moderately implemented
4. Accept in general	4. Strongly implemented
5. Endorse completely	5. Fully implemented

Principles—Health Services

	Degree Acceptance	Degree Implementation
1. Health services seek to establish a safe and healthful school environment	1 2 3 4 5	1 2 3 4 5
2. Health services are so coordinated to provide continuous aid to the growth and development of students and to the protection and improvement of their health	1 2 3 4 5	1 2 3 4 5
3. All staff members are encouraged to regard the school health program as a cooperative undertaking designed to help students understand and develop healthful living habits	1 2 3 4 5	1 2 3 4 5
4. All students and teachers are informed regarding the procedures they should follow in case of injury or illness	1 2 3 4 5	1 2 3 4 5
5. First aid supplies are conveniently available	1 2 3 4 5	1 2 3 4 5
6. Parents are informed and other necessary actions taken when a student is seriously injured or ill	1 2 3 4 5	1 2 3 4 5
7. Students are referred to the family doctor or dentist for follow-up services after periodic screening tests	1 2 3 4 5	1 2 3 4 5
8. Rehabilitation services are obtained when appropriate and possible	1 2 3 4 5	1 2 3 4 5
9. Provision is made for the exchange of essential information among community health sources, students, parents and appropriate school personnel	1 2 3 4 5	1 2 3 4 5
10. Regular reports are made to the principal regarding the general type of health services provided to the students. All accidents are reported regularly for accident prevention and liability analysis	1 2 3 4 5	1 2 3 4 5
11. Well planned procedures for periodic evaluation of the school health services are provided	1 2 3 4 5	1 2 3 4 5

12. Other

II. Description of the Program

A. How are the health services organized and administered?

B. What preparation, experience and personal qualifications are represented by the health services staff?

C. List, by position, the health service personnel available to the school and indicate how their time is utilized by the school.

D. Describe the health service facilities and discuss their adequacy.

E. What provisions are made for obtaining information about students relative to:

1. Home and family?

2. Health and medical status?

F. What measures exist to protect the integrity of the individual's health record for authorized and professional use only?

G. Describe the health service activities that are designed to encourage good mental, emotional and social health practices.

H. Describe the provisions made to accommodate the handicapped student.

I. Discuss the following health-service-related situations:

1. The instructional and supervisory activities of teachers that promote health and safety.

2. The adequacy of handwashing facilities (including hot water, soap and towels) available at all times in each washroom throughout the school.

3. The provision of locker room facilities, materials and equipment designed to maintain and promote health and safety.

4. In addition to the school nurse, to what extent do school personnel hold current first aid certificates?

J. List the measures taken to eliminate practices that are detrimental to student health such as poor nutritional habits, the use of tobacco, alcoholic beverages or drugs. Give evidences of the effectiveness of the means used.

K. Comments (add any other comments concerning the school's health services):

III. Evaluation

A. Cite evidence that the health services are consistent with the school's stated philosophy and objectives.

B. What improvements in the health services have been completed within the past three years?

C. What are the areas of special strength in the health services?

D. Identify those areas of the health services that are in greatest need of strengthening.

E. What procedures and practices are used in the continuous evaluation of the health services?

IV. Plans for Improvement

A. List, in order of priority, the short-range improvements planned for the school health services.

B. List, in order of priority, the long-range improvements that are planned for the school health services.

C. Explain, citing specific reasons, why any of these desirable changes seem unattainable.

V. Current Status Scale

On the scale please indicate with a check mark the present status of the health services in relation to the school's stated philosophy and objectives.

Much		Little or No
Improvement		Improvement
Needed		Needed

Comments (add any other comments concerning the current status of the school's health services):

AUXILIARY SERVICES: FOOD

A. Describe the food services provided for the students of this school.

B. Describe the adequacy of the food service facilities and related functions:

1. Dining area (including aesthetic aspects)

2. Food preparation area

3. Provisions for sanitation and cleanliness

4. Provisions for offering appetizing and nutritionally balanced meals

5. Provisions for student training in acceptable conduct

C. Describe the process for selecting, training and evaluating the people involved in food services.

D. What improvements in the school's food services have been completed in the past three years?

E. What plans exist for improving the food services within the next three years?

F. What other improvements do you feel would be necessary to make the food services ideal for this school? If you feel that any of these desirable changes seem unattainable by your school, explain why.

G. On the scale indicate with a check mark the present status of the food services in relation to the school's stated philosophy and objectives.

Much
Improvement
Needed

Little or No
Improvement
Needed

Comments (add any other comments concerning the current status of the food services):

AUXILIARY SERVICES: TRANSPORTATION

A. Describe the transportation services provided by the school.

B. What percent of students use each of the following modes of transportation?

    1. School-operated busses   _____ %

    2. Public conveyance   _____ %

    3. Walk or ride bicycles   _____ %

    4. Private automobiles   _____ %

C. What measures are taken to maximize each student's safety to and from school?

D. What provision is made for student training in acceptable conduct?

E. How do the transportation services of the school accommodate the school program in such matters as field trips, student activities, etc.?

F. Describe the processes for selection, training and evaluating the people involved in transportation services.

G. What have been the improvements in the school's transportation services in the past three years?

H. What plans exist for improving the transportation services within the next three years?

I. Explain, citing specific reasons, why any of these desirable changes seem unattainable.

J. On the scale indicate with a check mark the present status of the transportation services in relation to the school's stated philosophy and objectives.

Much
Improvement
Needed

Little or No
Improvement
Needed

Comments (add any other comments concerning the current status of the transportation services):

AUXILIARY SERVICES: OTHER

AUXILIARY SERVICES: OTHER

Student Activities Program

NAME OF SCHOOL_____

DATE_____

Prepared by

_____   _____

_____   _____

_____   _____

The committee given the responsibility for completing this section will find it beneficial to become thoroughly familiar with the entire section before attempting to react or respond to any part of it.

The committee should recognize that Sections N and O, titled "School and Community" and "Philosophy and Objectives," taken together form the foundation for the total evaluation. The responses in all other sections should reflect an awareness of the characteristics of both the school and the community and the influence of the statement of philosophy and objectives.

Although space has been provided throughout the section for committee responses, statements need not be limited to that space; the committee should feel free to attach addenda for items whose clarity will be improved by fuller development.

The report of this committee, when completed, should be presented to the entire faculty for approval or modification.

NATIONAL STUDY OF SCHOOL EVALUATION
5201 Leesburg Pike, Falls Church, Virginia 22041

Organization of the Criteria

The *Secondary School Evaluative Criteria: Narrative Edition* (Revised) is composed of fourteen sections as follows:

M   Manual
N1   School and Community (Public Schools)
N2   School and Community (Nonpublic Schools)
O   Phliosophy and Objectives
P   Design of Curriculum
Q   Instructional Areas
R   Individual Faculty Data
S   School Staff and Administration
T   Learning Media Services
U   Guidance Services
V   Auxiliary Services
W   Student Activities Program
X   School Plant and Facilities
Y   Plans and Priorities

The "Manual" provides an overview of the evaluation process and explains in some detail how the materials may be used. The section on "School and Community" together with the section on "Philosophy and Objectives" form the foundation for the process and undergird the entire evaluation.

"School and Community" is a data-gathering section. The section "School and Community (Nonpublic Schools)" is designed specifically for use by independent, church-related and other nonpublic schools. "Philosophy and Objectives" is designed to assist in developing or reexamining the school's existing philosophy and objectives in light of the data provided by the "School and Community" section.

The next two sections, "Design of Curriculum" and "Instructional Areas," are also closely related. "Design of Curriculum" focuses on the organization of the curriculum. It is extremely important that the subcommittee completing this section is a representative body of the total school program. The "Instructional Areas" section makes possible the evaluation of each of the areas of learning that the school identifies.

The section on "Individual Faculty Data" includes data concerning individual faculty members and provides opportunity for those persons to express opinions on certain aspects of the school program. This is the only section that each faculty member completes individually. The "School Staff and Administration" section gives attention to administration, instructional staff and auxiliary staff. The "Learning Media Services" section includes media services, library and audio-visual services. The "Guidance Services" section includes information about personal, educational and career counseling and the guidance program. The section entitled "Auxiliary Services" examines such services as those dealing with health, food and transportation. The "Student Activities Program" section focuses on the school's total activities program. The next section deals with the school plant and facilities. The final section, "Plans and Priorities," provides an opportunity to place in priority the school's plans for improvement.

The sections P, Q, S, T, U, V, W, and X use this common format:

   I. Principles
  II. Description
 III. Evaluation
 IV. Plans for Improvement
  V. Current Status Scale

This five-point format begins with Part I, a series of principles designed to stimulate thought and reflection about the school program. Part II consists of probing questions designed to elicit a description of the program or area under consideration. Part III provides an opportunity to appraise and evaluate the program described in the second part and Part IV asks for the school's plans for improvement. Part V gives the school an opportunity to indicate its status in comparison to an "optimum" program.

The School's Task in Evaluation

The complete evaluation of a school as recommended by the National Study of School Evaluation is a three-step process. The first step is a self-evaluation carried out by the faculty of the individual school. This step usually requires a minimum of one year. The second step is an evaluation by a visiting committee, which usually requires a minimum of three days. The third step is the school's consideration and follow-up of the findings of the evaluation.

The National Study of School Evaluation has developed a means for recognizing that schools which are quite different may be equally sound educationally. This concept involves the basic principle that a school shall be evaluated in terms of what it is striving to accomplish (its philosophy and objectives) and according to the extent to which it is meeting the needs of the students who are enrolled or for whom it is responsible. The philosophy and objectives of the school must be acceptable to some agency (a community, an accrediting association, a state department of education) if the evaluation is to be recognized beyond the confines of the school.

School staff and administration, parents, students and members of the governing body should be actively involved in this self-evaluation. It is important that all who are involved understand that the purpose of this self-study is to improve the quality of the school's program through the means of self-evaluation and comprehensive examination of what is happening to students in the school environment.

It is important to recognize that no one section of the self-study is meant to stand alone. Each section has been designed to correlate with other sections to form a comprehensive self-evaluation. It is important that participants not become single-minded when working on a particular section and overlook the fact that the total evaluation does not rest on that particular section. Staff interaction is essential in bringing about change.

This instrument is designed for a wide variety of secondary schools. Therefore, some items may not be applicable to a particular school situation. Schools are reminded of their prerogative to strike or change words, so long as they do not misdirect the intent of a statement but render it more relevant. In the event that an entire statement appears to be irrelevant, a school may decide it does not apply and explain its view in the space provided.

Finally, it is vital that each evaluation participant receives feedback on reports of all sections of the self-study and that each participant have an opportunity to express either agreement or disagreement with each report. Provision should be made for modification of a report when advisable.

More detailed information may be found in the "Manual," Section M.

I. Principles

Introduction

For purposes of this instrument, a student activity is defined as any school-sponsored endeavor which involves students and for which neither a grade nor academic credit is given.

The student activities program should be an integral part of the educational program and should be related to the needs of students. It should provide students with opportunities to explore and develop their interests and talents; assist them to develop physically, emotionally, intellectually and socially; and promote positive attitudes toward work and the use of leisure time. A broad program of student activities should enhance the total educational program.

Listed below are a number of principles regarding student activities that are generally held to be valid and to which the school community should address itself. This introduction is designed to encourage introspection concerning this section of the self-study. It is a starting point for discussion and for interaction among participants preparatory to delving into the nature of this aspect of the school program. Participants should avoid lengthy debate over the adequacy or the inadequacy of each principle. Rather, it is important that the committee assigned this responsibility react to each statement in terms of an overview of how the school community generally accepts and implements each principle.

Indicate by circling the appropriate number in the first column to the right of each principle the degree to which that principle is accepted by the school and indicate by circling the appropriate number in the second column the degree to which that principle is implemented in the school. Where necessary, in order to be consistent with the school's stated philosophy and objectives, principles may be modified and others added.

The descriptions of the numbers listed immediately below apply to the numbers in the columns to the right of the principles and should be borne in mind when marking the degree of acceptance and the degree of implementation.

Degree of Acceptance
1. Unacceptable
2. Questionable
3. Accept with reservations
4. Accept in general
5. Endorse completely

Degree of Implementation
1. Not implemented
2. Weakly implemented
3. Moderately implemented
4. Strongly implemented
5. Fully implemented

Principles

The student activities program:

	Degree of Acceptance	Degree of Implementation
1. Is oriented toward and is comprehensive enough to meet the needs and interests of secondary school students.	1 2 3 4 5	1 2 3 4 5
2. Is a means of implementing, accomplishing and reflecting the philosophy and objectives of the school.	1 2 3 4 5	1 2 3 4 5
3. Provides experiences that enhance the opportunity to develop increasing responsibility, initiative, leadership, cooperation and self-direction.	1 2 3 4 5	1 2 3 4 5
4. Provides students with exploration experiences that have physical, social, intellectual and emotional value for both the present and the future.	1 2 3 4 5	1 2 3 4 5
5. Provides leisure-time and recreational experiences that will have both immediate and carry-over value.	1 2 3 4 5	1 2 3 4 5
6. Provides activities for individuals, small-groups and the entire student body.	1 2 3 4 5	1 2 3 4 5
7. Provides a form of student participation in school government as an important feature of the program.	1 2 3 4 5	1 2 3 4 5
8. Avoids emphasis on contests and the exploitation of students for the benefit of school or community prestige.	1 2 3 4 5	1 2 3 4 5
9. Does not restrict participation on the basis of social or financial factors.	1 2 3 4 5	1 2 3 4 5
10. Is an integral part of the educational program.	1 2 3 4 5	1 2 3 4 5

	Degree Acceptance					Degree Implementation				

11. Is in proper proportion within the educational program in relation to teacher time, student time, school emphasis, school budget, facilities, etc.................   1 2 3 4 5 | 1 2 3 4 5

12. Generally has the activities scheduled as part of the regular school day........   1 2 3 4 5 | 1 2 3 4 5

13. Is under the supervision of interested, competent and qualified sponsors.......   1 2 3 4 5 | 1 2 3 4 5

14. Is recognized by the faculty as a worthwhile endeavor......................   1 2 3 4 5 | 1 2 3 4 5

15. Is under the complete control of the school, administratively and financially.....   1 2 3 4 5 | 1 2 3 4 5

16. Involves students in the decision-making process.........................   1 2 3 4 5 | 1 2 3 4 5

17. Provides orientation for students new to the program......................   1 2 3 4 5 | 1 2 3 4 5

18. Is continually evaluated by students, faculty and administration..............   1 2 3 4 5 | 1 2 3 4 5

19. Others

II. Description of the Program

A. Complete the following tables:

TABLE I
Clubs and Organizations

CLUBS AND ORGANIZATIONS	Grade Levels	PARTICIPANTS			How Selected	Amount Budgeted	Names of Sponsors
		Number					
		Boys	Girls	Total			

TABLE II
Intramurals

TYPES OF INTRAMURALS	Grade Levels	PARTICIPANTS			How Selected	Amount Budgeted	Names of Sponsors
		Number					
		Boys	Girls	Total			

TABLE III
Interscholastic Athletics

TYPES OF INTERSCHOOL ATHLETICS	Grade Levels	PARTICIPANTS			How Selected	Amount Budgeted	Names of Coaches	Total Number of Games	Number of Night Games	If Admission is charged, How Much?	When is practice held? (Time of day)
		Number		Total							
		Boys	Girls								

TABLE IV
Other Activities
(such as music, drama, forensics)

| TYPES OF OTHER ACTIVITIES | Grade Levels | PARTICIPANTS | | | | Amount Budgeted | Names of Sponsors | Total Number of Performances | Number of Night Performances | If Admission is charged, How much? | When is practice held? (Time of day) |
| | | Number | | | How Selected | | | | | | |
		Boys	Girls	Total							

B. A copy of the following form is to be filled out by each activity sponsor. (Schools may make as many copies of this page as needed.)

NAME OF ACTIVITY_____

Name of Sponsor_____

  1. Objectives:

  2. What problems, if any, were encountered in attempting to meet the objectives during the past year?

  3. Indicate the length of meetings or practice sessions, frequency of meetings or practice sessions and duration (montns per year) of the activity.

  4. How are the outcomes (physical, emotional, intellectual and social development of students) measured and evaluated to determine the relationship to the objectives?

5. Attach a copy of the rules or bylaws governing the activity.

C. Supply the informatioon requested. (Use additional sheets if necessary)
   1. Student participation

	Student Activities Participants (Count each participant only once)
a. Total School Enrollment	
Boys _____	Boys _____
Girls _____	Girls _____
Total _____	Total _____

   b. In what ways are exceptional students involved in the school's activities program?

   2. Describe any past or current studies to determine which students do not participate and the reason for their lack of participation.

   3. What provision is made for the less talented students to participate in formal and/or informal music, speech, drama and other such activities?

4. List the dates and the program for each of the four most recent school assemblies. How did these assemblies contribute to the school's philosophy and objectives?

5. In what ways do students participate in assembly programs?

6. In what specific ways do students have a voice in school government?

7. Are any activities, believed to be overemphasized to the extent that they take a disproportionate amount of student and school time? (If "yes," identify and cite possible contributing factors.)

8. Is there sufficient guidance to ensure against overparticipation on the part of individual students? Explain.

9. What publications does the school sponsor? (Attach copies) To what extent are students involved? How is each publication financed?

10. Describe how the funds for the activities program are provided, disbursed and controlled. (Attach annual financial report of the activities program.)

11. What percent of the faculty members sponsor an activity? How are they selected or recruited?

12. Are there any nonschool personnel sponsoring student activities? How are they selected or recruited?

13. When is time provided for clubs and other activities?

14. What are the procedures for:

    a. Starting a new activity?

    b. Terminating an existing activity?

15. In what way is participation regulated in contests and activities organized by outside agencies?

16. In what ways does the activities program foster school spirit, loyalty and good sportsmanship?

17. In what ways does the activities program provide organized instruction in the development of social skills and interpersonal relationships?

18. Show evidence that the activities program encourages development of special talents and interests.

19. In what ways does the homeroom or related program, if any, make specific contributions to the student activities objectives?

20. What provisions are made for proper equipment and safety in the activities program?

21. Describe provisions made for recognition of student participation, service and achievement in the activities program.

22. If salary supplements are paid to sponsors or coaches, are such supplements governed by board policy and the administrative head of the school?

23. In systems having a centralized director of athletics and physical education, are decisions on programs, sports, games and professional personnel made with full participation and concurrence of the school administrator and appropriate faculty members?

D. Comments (add any other comments concerning the school's student activities program):

III. Evaluation

A. What evidence exists that the school and the district place positive and reasonable priority on student activities?

B. Cite evidence that the student activities program is consistent with the school's stated philosophy and objectives.

C. What improvements in the student activities program have been accomplished within the past three years?

D. What are the areas of special strength in the student activities program?

E. Identify those areas of the student activities program that are in greatest need of strengthening.

F. What part, if any, of the student activities program is over-emphasized? What action should be taken to achieve balance?

IV. Plans for Improvement

A. List, in order of priority, the short-range improvements planned for the student activities program.

B. List, in order of priority, the long-range improvements that are planned for the student activities program.

C. Explain, citing specific reasons, why any of these desirable changes seem unattainable.

V. Current Status Scale

On the scale indicate with a check mark the present status of the student activities program in relation to the school's philosophy and objectives.

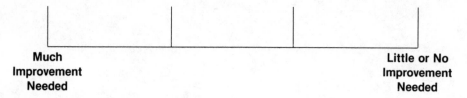

	Much Improvement Needed			Little or No Improvement Needed

Comment (add any other comments concerning the current status of the school's student activities program):

School Plant and Facilities

NAME OF SCHOOL_____

DATE_____

Prepared by

_____   _____

_____   _____

_____   _____

    The committee given the responsibility for completing this section will find it beneficial to become thoroughly familiar with the entire section before attempting to react or respond to any part of it.

    The committee should recognize that Sections N and O, titled "School and Community" and "Philosophy and Objectives," taken together form the foundation for the total evaluation. The responses in all other sections should reflect an awareness of the characteristics of both the school and the community and the influence of the statement of philosophy and objectives.

    Although space has been provided throughout the section for committee responses, statements need not be limited to that space; the committee should feel free to attach addenda for items whose clarity will be improved by fuller development.

    The report of this committee, when completed, should be presented to the entire faculty for approval or modification.

NATIONAL STUDY OF SCHOOL EVALUATION
5201 Leesburg Pike, Falls Church, Virginia 22041

Organization of the Criteria

The *Secondary School Evaluative Criteria: Narrative Edition* (Revised) is composed of fourteen sections as follows:

M   Manual
N1 School and Community (Public Schools)
N2 School and Community (Nonpublic Schools)
O   Phliosophy and Objectives
P   Design of Curriculum
Q   Instructional Areas
R   Individual Faculty Data
S   School Staff and Administration
T   Learning Media Services
U   Guidance Services
V   Auxiliary Services
W   Student Activities Program
X   School Plant and Facilities
Y   Plans and Priorities

The "Manual" provides an overview of the evaluation process and explains in some detail how the materials may be used. The section on "School and Community" together with the section on "Philosophy and Objectives" form the foundation for the process and undergird the entire evaluation.

"School and Community" is a data-gathering section. The section "School and Community (Nonpublic Schools)" is designed specifically for use by independent, church-related and other nonpublic schools. "Philosophy and Objectives" is designed to assist in developing or reexamining the school's existing philosophy and objectives in light of the data provided by the "School and Community" section.

The next two sections, "Design of Curriculum" and "Instructional Areas," are also closely related. "Design of Curriculum" focuses on the organization of the curriculum. It is extremely important that the subcommittee completing this section is a representative body of the total school program. The "Instructional Areas" section makes possible the evaluation of each of the areas of learning that the school identifies.

The section on "Individual Faculty Data" includes data concerning individual faculty members and provides opportunity for those persons to express opinions on certain aspects of the school program. This is the only section that each faculty member completes individually. The "School Staff and Administration" section gives attention to administration, instructional staff and auxiliary staff. The "Learning Media Services" section includes media services, library and audio-visual services. The "Guidance Services" section includes information about personal, educational and career counseling and the guidance program. The section entitled "Auxiliary Services" examines such services as those dealing with health, food and transportation. The "Student Activities Program" section focuses on the school's total activities program. The next section deals with the school plant and facilities. The final section, "Plans and Priorities," provides an opportunity to place in priority the school's plans for improvement.

The sections P, Q, S, T, U, V, W, and X use this common format:

  I. Principles
  II. Description
  III. Evaluation
  IV. Plans for Improvement
  V. Current Status Scale

This five-point format begins with Part I, a series of principles designed to stimulate thought and reflection about the school program. Part II consists of probing questions designed to elicit a description of the program or area under consideration. Part III provides an opportunity to appraise and evaluate the program described in the second part and Part IV asks for the school's plans for improvement. Part V gives the school an opportunity to indicate its status in comparison to an "optimum" program.

The School's Task in Evaluation

The complete evaluation of a school as recommended by the National Study of School Evaluation is a three-step process. The first step is a self-evaluation carried out by the faculty of the individual school. This step usually requires a minimum of one year. The second step is an evaluation by a visiting committee, which usually requires a minimum of three days. The third step is the school's consideration and follow-up of the findings of the evaluation.

The National Study of School Evaluation has developed a means for recognizing that schools which are quite different may be equally sound educationally. This concept involves the basic principle that a school shall be evaluated in terms of what it is striving to accomplish (its philosophy and objectives) and according to the extent to which it is meeting the needs of the students who are enrolled or for whom it is responsible. The philosophy and objectives of the school must be acceptable to some agency (a community, an accrediting association, a state department of education) if the evaluation is to be recognized beyond the confines of the school.

School staff and administration, parents, students and members of the governing body should be actively involved in this self-evaluation. It is important that all who are involved understand that the purpose of this self-study is to improve the quality of the school's program through the means of self-evaluation and comprehensive examination of what is happening to students in the school environment.

It is important to recognize that no one section of the self-study is meant to stand alone. Each section has been designed to correlate with other sections to form a comprehensive self-evaluation. It is important that participants not become single-minded when working on a particular section and overlook the fact that the total evaluation does not rest on that particular section. Staff interaction is essential in bringing about change.

This instrument is designed for a wide variety of secondary schools. Therefore, some items may not be applicable to a particular school situation. Schools are reminded of their prerogative to strike or change words, so long as they do not misdirect the intent of a statement but render it more relevant. In the event that an entire statement appears to be irrelevant, a school may decide it does not apply and explain its view in the space provided.

Finally, it is vital that each evaluation participant receives feedback on reports of all sections of the self-study and that each participant have an opportunity to express either agreement or disagreement with each report. Provision should be made for modification of a report when advisable.

More detailed information may be found in the "Manual," Section M.

I. Principles

Introduction

The school's physical plant, consisting of the site, building, equipment and services, is an important factor in the functioning of the educational program. The plant, as constructed and equipped, is more than a place of instruction. It is, during school time, the physical environment which assists or limits student achievement of desirable learning outcomes.

Because the school plant serves as a vehicle in the implementation of the total educational program, its design should be based on, and consistent with, the stated philosophy and objectives of the school. It should include extensive provisions for the health and safety of all persons involved as well as incorporate aesthetic features that contribute to a positive educational atmosphere.

Listed below are a number of specific principles regarding the "School Plant" to which administration, faculty, parents and students should address themselves. This introductory part is designed to encourage introspection concerning this section of the self-study. It is a starting point for discussion and for interaction among participants preparatory to delving into the nature of this aspect of the school program. Participants should avoid lengthy debate over the adequacy or the inadequacy of each principle. Rather, it is important that the committee assigned this responsibility react to each statement in terms of an overview of how the school community generally accepts and implements each principle.

The committee should indicate by circling the appropriate number in the first column to the right of each principle the extent to which that principle is accepted by the school and indicate by circling the appropriate number in the second column the extent to which that principle is being implemented in the school. Where necessary, in order to be consistent with the stated philosophy and objectives, specific principles may be modified and others added.

The descriptions of the numbers listed immediately below apply to the numbers in the columns to the right of the principles and should be borne in mind when marking the degree of acceptance and the degree of implementation.

Degree of Acceptance

1. Unacceptable
2. Questionable
3. Accept with reservations
4. Accept in general
5. Endorse completely

Degree of Implementation

1. Not implemented
2. Weakly implemented
3. Moderately implemented
4. Strongly implemented
5. Fully implemented

Principles

	Degree of Acceptance	Degree of Implementation
1. The school plant is designed and built to make possible the effective carrying out of the educational program of the school in terms of the philosophy and objectives of the school..........	1 2 3 4 5	1 2 3 4 5
2. The design of the school plant provides for present and future flexibility as		
a. the educational program changes...............	1 2 3 4 5	1 2 3 4 5
b. the enrollment pattern changes...............	1 2 3 4 5	1 2 3 4 5
3. The school plant has aesthetic qualities that serve to enhance the learning experiences of the students...............	1 2 3 4 5	1 2 3 4 5
4. The school plant contains provisions for instructional groups of varying sizes...	1 2 3 4 5	1 2 3 4 5
5. The heating and ventilating systems of the building meet recommended health and comfort standards...............	1 2 3 4 5	1 2 3 4 5
6. The lighting of the building meets approved standards...............	1 2 3 4 5	1 2 3 4 5
7. Instructional and service areas that involve noise-producing activities are separated from the quieter classrooms or acoustically treated to reduce noise transference...............	1 2 3 4 5	1 2 3 4 5
8. Compliance with federal health and safety codes ensures student and staff health and safety...............	1 2 3 4 5	1 2 3 4 5
9. The design of the building		
a. Provides for accessibility by the handicapped...............	1 2 3 4 5	1 2 3 4 5
b. Facilitates the efficient movement of students...............	1 2 3 4 5	1 2 3 4 5
c. Provides for adequate security features...............	1 2 3 4 5	1 2 3 4 5
d. Provides for emergency exits...............	1 2 3 4 5	1 2 3 4 5

	Degree Acceptance					Degree Implementation				

10. Adequate storage areas are readily accessible to

a. Classroom teachers	1	2	3	4	5	1	2	3	4	5
b. Students	1	2	3	4	5	1	2	3	4	5
c. Clerical staff	1	2	3	4	5	1	2	3	4	5
d. Custodial staff	1	2	3	4	5	1	2	3	4	5

11. The building(s) and outdoor facilities are located on the site for both functional qualities and aesthetic appreciation.   1 2 3 4 5   1 2 3 4 5

12. The school site reflects professional planning for

a. Location	1	2	3	4	5	1	2	3	4	5
b. Access roads or streets	1	2	3	4	5	1	2	3	4	5
c. Pedestrian traffic (where applicable)	1	2	3	4	5	1	2	3	4	5
d. Bus loading and unloading (where applicable)	1	2	3	4	5	1	2	3	4	5
e. Parking areas	1	2	3	4	5	1	2	3	4	5
f. Outdoor educational facilities	1	2	3	4	5	1	2	3	4	5
g. Public utilities	1	2	3	4	5	1	2	3	4	5
h. Drainage	1	2	3	4	5	1	2	3	4	5
i. Landscape	1	2	3	4	5	1	2	3	4	5
j. Energy conservation	1	2	3	4	5	1	2	3	4	5

13. Equipment and facilities for food service are well-designed for needs of the program.   1 2 3 4 5   1 2 3 4 5

14. Maintenance and daily cleanliness are well-planned and consistently carried out.   1 2 3 4 5   1 2 3 4 5

15. Others

II. Description of Facilities

A. Discuss the compatibility of the building design in general with the philosophy and objectives of the school. Indicate the student capacity for which the building was planned.

B. Discuss the adequacy of the following specific areas of the physical facility in relation to (a) the educational program and (b) the school enrollment, where applicable. Comments here should summarize the findings of the Instructional Area Committees.

　　1. Classrooms

　　2. Small-group rooms (conference and instructional)

　　3. Laboratories

4. Career education, vocational education and industrial education facilities

5. Independent study areas

6. Areas for activities of exceptional students

7. Learning media center

8. Auditorium

9. Physical education facilities

10. Athletic facilities

11. Food service areas

12. Offices, workrooms and restrooms for teachers

13. Administrative offices

14. Outdoor areas (instructional and other)

15. Other

C. Are the following facilities adequate in number to meet the personal needs of the students? Are they maintained in proper working order?
   1. Lockers

   2. Washroom and toilet areas

   3. Drinking fountains

D. Discuss the extent to which safety features have been incorporated in the school plant. Include safeguards against fire, tornado and earthquake.

E. Describe security measures relating to the school plant.

F. Comments (add any other comments concerning the school plant and facilities):

III. Evaluation

A. What are the most important features of the school plant that enhance the educational program?

B. What are the most important features of the school plant that detract from the educational program?

C. Discuss the adequacy of the maintenance program in terms of:
   1. Appearance of the building

   2. Appearance of the grounds

   3. Custodial work areas

D. What continuous evaluation procedures are used to ensure that the best possible use is being made of the existing school plant in implementing the philosophy and objectives of the school?

IV. Plans for Improvement

A. List, in order of priority, the short-range plans for improvement of the school plant.

B. List, in order of priority, the long-range plans for the improvement of the school plant. Give the current status of the plans.

C. Explain, citing specific reasons, why any of these desirable changes seem unattainable.

V. Current Status Scale

On the scale indicate with a check mark the present status of your school plant in relation to the school's stated philosophy and objectives and the community it serves.

**Much
Improvement
Needed**

**Little or No
Improvement
Needed**

Comments (add any other comments concerning the school plant):

Plans and Priorities

NAME OF SCHOOL_____

DATE_____

Prepared by

_____   _____

_____   _____

_____   _____

The committee given the responsibility of completing this section will need to be thoroughly familiar with all aspects of the self-study. Schools may wish to have the steering committee accept this responsibility. This section is to be completed at the conclusion of the self-study when the committee and the school faculty may wish to review and possibly modify the school's plans for improvement.

It is important to remember that two of the most significant reasons for conducting this self-study are (1) the identification of problems or areas of weakness in the school program that should be remedied and (2) the projection of plans for remediation. The implementation of these plans becomes the task of the faculty during the interval between completion of this self-study and the beginning of the next comprehensive self-study. It is understood that these plans and priorities may be changed or modified by the governing body when the final plan of action is agreed upon.

NATIONAL STUDY OF SCHOOL EVALUATION
5201 Leesburg Pike, Falls Church, Virginia 22041

Organization of the Criteria

The *Secondary School Evaluative Criteria: Narrative Edition* (Revised) is composed of fourteen sections as follows:

M   Manual
N1   School and Community (Public Schools)
N2   School and Community (Nonpublic Schools)
O   Phliosophy and Objectives
P   Design of Curriculum
Q   Instructional Areas
R   Individual Faculty Data
S   School Staff and Administration
T   Learning Media Services
U   Guidance Services
V   Auxiliary Services
W   Student Activities Program
X   School Plant and Facilities
Y   Plans and Priorities

The "Manual" provides an overview of the evaluation process and explains in some detail how the materials may be used. The section on "School and Community" together with the section on "Philosophy and Objectives" form the foundation for the process and undergird the entire evaluation.

"School and Community" is a data-gathering section. The section "School and Community (Nonpublic Schools)" is designed specifically for use by independent, church-related and other nonpublic schools. "Philosophy and Objectives" is designed to assist in developing or reexamining the school's existing philosophy and objectives in light of the data provided by the "School and Community" section.

The next two sections, "Design of Curriculum" and "Instructional Areas," are also closely related. "Design of Curriculum" focuses on the organization of the curriculum. It is extremely important that the subcommittee completing this section is a representative body of the total school program. The "Instructional Areas" section makes possible the evaluation of each of the areas of learning that the school identifies.

The section on "Individual Faculty Data" includes data concerning individual faculty members and provides opportunity for those persons to express opinions on certain aspects of the school program. This is the only section that each faculty member completes individually. The "School Staff and Administration" section gives attention to administration, instructional staff and auxiliary staff. The "Learning Media Services" section includes media services, library and audio-visual services. The "Guidance Services" section includes information about personal, educational and career counseling and the guidance program. The section entitled "Auxiliary Services" examines such services as those dealing with health, food and transportation. The "Student Activities Program" section focuses on the school's total activities program. The next section deals with the school plant and facilities. The final section, "Plans and Priorities," provides an opportunity to place in priority the school's plans for improvement.

The sections P, Q, S, T, U, V, W, and X use this common format:

    I. Principles
   II. Description
  III. Evaluation
  IV. Plans for Improvement
   V. Current Status Scale

This five-point format begins with Part I, a series of principles designed to stimulate thought and reflection about the school program. Part II consists of probing questions designed to elicit a description of the program or area under consideration. Part III provides an opportunity to appraise and evaluate the program described in the second part and Part IV asks for the school's plans for improvement. Part V gives the school an opportunity to indicate its status in comparison to an "optimum" program.

The School's Task in Evaluation

The complete evaluation of a school as recommended by the National Study of School Evaluation is a three-step process. The first step is a self-evaluation carried out by the faculty of the individual school. This step usually requires a minimum of one year. The second step is an evaluation by a visiting committee, which usually requires a minimum of three days. The third step is the school's consideration and follow-up of the findings of the evaluation.

The National Study of School Evaluation has developed a means for recognizing that schools which are quite different may be equally sound educationally. This concept involves the basic principle that a school shall be evaluated in terms of what it is striving to accomplish (its philosophy and objectives) and according to the extent to which it is meeting the needs of the students who are enrolled or for whom it is responsible. The philosophy and objectives of the school must be acceptable to some agency (a community, an accrediting association, a state department of education) if the evaluation is to be recognized beyond the confines of the school.

School staff and administration, parents, students and members of the governing body should be actively involved in this self-evaluation. It is important that all who are involved understand that the purpose of this self-study is to improve the quality of the school's program through the means of self-evaluation and comprehensive examination of what is happening to students in the school environment.

It is important to recognize that no one section of the self-study is meant to stand alone. Each section has been designed to correlate with other sections to form a comprehensive self-evaluation. It is important that participants not become single-minded when working on a particular section and overlook the fact that the total evaluation does not rest on that particular section. Staff interaction is essential in bringing about change.

This instrument is designed for a wide variety of secondary schools. Therefore, some items may not be applicable to a particular school situation. Schools are reminded of their prerogative to strike or change words, so long as they do not misdirect the intent of a statement but render it more relevant. In the event that an entire statement appears to be irrelevant, a school may decide it does not apply and explain its view in the space provided.

Finally, it is vital that each evaluation participant receives feedback on reports of all sections of the self-study and that each participant have an opportunity to express either agreement or disagreement with each report. Provision should be made for modification of a report when advisable.

More detailed information may be found in the "Manual," Section M.

SUMMARY OF FOLLOW-UP PLANS INDICATING PRIORITIES

During this self-study, the faculty has already identified many problems or areas of weakness and has projected many plans for remedying the situation (see the faculty's responses to questions in Part III, "Evaluation" and Part IV, "Plans for Improvement").

The task now remains for the faculty to review all of those plans and to make decisions that will result in logical, sequential efforts to improve the overall school program.

A. Short-Range Plans

Immediately or within a two-year span of time, the school staff and administration will take leadership in effecting the following improvements (list in order of priority). Limit the number of plans to those that can be realistically achieved.

1.

2.

3.

4.

5.

6.

Add supplemental pages if needed.

B. Long-Range Plans

    Within a five-year period following the initial self-study, the school staff and administration will take leadership in effecting the following improvements (list in order of priority). Limit the number of plans to those that can be realistically achieved.

    1.

    2.

    3.

4.

5.

6.

Add supplemental pages if needed.